RAILWAYS AND GEOGRAPHY

by

ANDREW C. O'DELL
M.Sc., F.R.S.E.

PROFESSOR OF GEOGRAPHY,
UNIVERSITY OF ABERDEEN

LONDON
HUTCHINSON'S UNIVERSITY LIBRARY

Hutchinson & Co. (Publishers) Ltd.

178-202 Great Portland Street, London, W.1

London   Melbourne   Sydney   Auckland
Bombay Johannesburg New York Toronto

First published 1956

Printed in Great Britain
by The Anchor Press, Ltd.,
Tiptree, Essex

To
Q. L. O.
for her tolerance

CONTENTS

CONTENTS

LIST OF MAPS

A railway is defined in the *Shorter Oxford Dictionary* as :

1. A way or road laid with rails (originally of wood, subsequently of iron or steel), on which the wheels of wagons containing heavy goods are made to run for ease of transport ; also the way composed of rails thus laid.
2. *spec.* A line or track consisting of iron or steel rails, on which carriages or wagons conveying passengers or goods are moved by a locomotive engine. Hence also, the whole organization necessary for the working of this, and the company or persons owning or managing it.

PREFACE

This volume is not an attempt to give a detailed review of every railway system of the world in relation to its geographical environment. Rather it is an endeavour in the space available, to portray, with reference to numerous and varied examples, the geographical factors which have influenced in different places, at different times, the construction and the operation of railways. A certain bias occurs in the selection of examples in that stress has been laid upon Britain and North America—the former because it was the land in which railways evolved and the latter because it was the first sub-continent to be effectively developed as a result of railway construction.

The book owes much to writers of technical articles and books. Every endeavour has been made to acknowledge particular items used from these sources and an apology is tendered for any inadvertently omitted. For over a quarter of a century collecting railway literature has been my hobby and it has not always been possible to identify a source.

I am greatly indebted for information given with unfailing courtesy by railwaymen in Canada, the United States, Australia, New Zealand, South and East Africa and Britain and by the Port Authority of New York City. Two persons who must be singled out for their particular assistance are Miss Elizabeth O. Cullen of the Association of American Railroads, who has helped me in countless ways, and Mr. P. C. Masefield for permission to incorporate material from his stimulating Presidential Address to the Institute of Transport. Acknowledgement is also due to the editors, Professors Wooldridge and East, and to Mrs. Ruth Klauber for their help and encouragement. Proof-reading would have been far more onerous but for the help given by my wife.

CHAPTER I

THE TRACK

EARLY records and archaeological evidence show that in the Babylonian and Greek eras roads were improved by laying parallel lines of smooth stone blocks to facilitate the passage of vehicles, whilst at Syracuse and elsewhere are roads with grooved tracks. To allow vehicles to pass were crossing-places and these stone tramways, the precursor of railways, are particularly interesting because they have a uniform gauge of just over 5 ft. A similar grooving to this gauge was found at the Pompeii excavations and the Romans carried this idea to Britain where on a Roman road grooves can be traced with a gauge of 4 ft. 8 in.

As Charles Lee showed in his study, *The Evolution of Railways*, an advance came in the mines of the Harz Mountains where wooden ore-hutches were pushed along wooden rails. Before the end of the sixteenth century rails were laid to carry coal from Nottinghamshire pits to the Trent navigation while a few years later there is reference to wagonways in Northumberland and in Shropshire. These wagonways, primitive as they were, had the rudiments of the modern railway with flanged wheels running on the surface of parallel rails. They permitted the export of what were then vast tonnages. Landlords whose land lay between the collieries and the shipment points did not sell a strip of land to the coalmaster but charged a wayleave rent. Some of the wagonways were constructed in a substantial manner with heavy earthworks in order to ease gradients and for one of these wagonways an embankment of 100 ft. high and a bridge with a span of 103 ft. were constructed before 1732: for over two centuries these works have been used to carry coal from Tanfield northwards to the Tyne.

Many of the early lines were made with timber rails—oak, ash or beech—but iron strips were laid along them in order to reduce the rate of wear. At Coalbrookdale in Shropshire cast-iron plates were laid in 1767, largely in order to find a use for the furnace output during a period of slack trade, and proved so useful that for a time it became a standard practice. In 1789 the first line to be made with all iron rails was that from Nanpanton to the Loughborough Canal and although liable to fracture, because they were made of cast iron, the design and metal were improved and so iron, and after 1865 steel displaced timber. The term *Iron Road* became synonymous for Railway and appears as such in European languages : *chemin de fer* (French), *eisenbahn* (German), *strada ferrata* (Italian), *ferrocarril* (Spanish) and *järnväg* (Swedish).

Outside Europe older methods persisted because of local conditions. In the eastern part of the United States timber was plentiful, whereas iron rails were an expensive import from England, and many lines were constructed of timber faced with strap-iron. These strips of iron, under the weight of traffic, could work loose and spring up through the floors of carriages, hence they were termed snake rails. In Australia iron-bark timber was used and to this day locomotives run on such squared timber rails to carry lumber out of forests in New South Wales.

The track is called the permanent way, by contrast with the temporary rails of the contractor, but it is far from permanent. On British Railways wear of about half an inch on the head is sufficient to condemn the rail. This may happen in a year, whereas on subsidiary lines a rail may remain for over 50 years. An 80 lb. to the yard rail in Natal, on the outside of a 300-ft. radius curve, was found to have a life of only three months but by using special steels and with careful use of check-rails the life is now three years. To reduce the wear at junctions and on electrified lines alloy steels, such as manganese, are used or else the heat-treated (*sorbitic*) rail is laid. Cross sections have been improved to give better service and the weight of the rail has been increased ; some heavy duty traffic lines in the U.S.A. are now laid with 159 lb. to the yard rail. In Britain the heaviest rail is 109 lb. One device to prolong the life is to oil the rails on sharp curves taking care that the oil does not reach the running surface and cause the driving wheels to slip. In the U.S.A. in one year alone (1926) 2·2 million tons of new rail were laid ; thus the incentive to increase the life is great.

Rails were originally laid in very short lengths but noise and wear can be reduced by welding rails together. It has been estimated in the U.S.A. that a welded rail-joint pays for itself in three years. On the Commonwealth lines in Australia 270 ft. is now the standard length and on the Elgin, Joliet and Eastern Railway[1] 140 lb. rails have been welded for 19,812 ft.

In the evolution of the track there was a period when it was thought that rigidity was essential and the use of timber sleepers, which hold the rails at correct gauge, was abandoned in favour of stone blocks, or, in a few cases, of spiking the rails directly on the floor of rock cuttings. Unfortunately many tons of the stone sleepers were quarried and laid, on the London and Birmingham Railway alone 152,460 tons of stone blocks were used, before it was realized that such a base was too rigid and resulted in rail fractures. When the first Kentucky line, that from Frankfort to Lexington, was begun in 1834 the permanent way consisted of 2-in.-wide iron strips fixed to limestone slabs by spikes set in lead but it was found that frost quickly disintegrated the limestone and so timber was substituted.

Timber, which gives elasticity to the track, is now normally treated with creosote or chemicals such as sodium arsenate or zinc chloride to prevent decay but even treated sleepers were found to last only a fortnight when laid on the Gold Coast line from Sekondi towards Tarkwa. The trade in timber for track purposes is very considerable : British railways, for example, lay annually $4\frac{1}{2}$ million sleepers which had to be imported. In South Africa local yellow-wood from the coastal belt is used together with imports of d'jatti from Java and jarrah from Western Australia. To reduce the imports, the railway administration of South Africa has created since 1902 extensive plantations of pine and eucalyptus. A single mile of main line track in Britain has 2,112 sleepers (measuring 10 in. by 5 in. by $8\frac{1}{2}$ ft.) and in South Africa about the same number to the mile but $1\frac{1}{2}$ ft. shorter. The average life of a main-line sleeper in Britain is 17 to 25 years, according to the timber, and in South Africa 15 to 20 years, therefore taking these two countries alone as representative samples, it is clear that the supply of timber is a major consideration. On the Class 1 railways of the United States nearly 60 million treated sleepers alone were laid in 1928 : there are about 990

[1] This line serves the Outer Belt of Chicago and, carrying freight only, is said to have the second busiest track, by car-miles, in the U.S.A.

million sleepers laid on these lines. The number relaid varies greatly from year to year but with the rising cost of timber untreated sleepers are becoming a thing of the past.[1] In countries such as Abyssinia, where even treated timber is quickly consumed by termites, iron or steel sleepers are used. Concrete has been tried in tropical countries and also in the temperate lands when, as in time of war, timber or steel is expensive or unobtainable. While concrete does not rot it is not satisfactory for it gives noisy running. Steel sleepers have been found to corrode rapidly in the humid air of the eastern coastal belt of South Africa. There is no one material which provides an ideal track but with proper maintenance it is possible to meet all demands for a safe track. In the earlier days the condition of the track led to modifications of the rolling stock, e.g. the lightly laid rough tracks of the pioneer American lines were only passable after the adoption of the bogie and equalizing beam which allowed the vehicles to "fit" themselves to the inequalities.

To give good drainage the lines are ballasted with a material which does not crumble and for this broken iron-furnace slag is ideal. Grease and dirt can choke the ballast and so it has to be either washed and replaced, for which process machines are now available, or else renewed. Without clean ballast fast running is dangerous. Weed growth is a problem and to reduce labour demands weed-killers are sprayed on the track. In Ratho cutting, on the Glasgow line eight miles east of Edinburgh, the gradient is so slight that water cannot run freely. The whinstone is impermeable and as a result the sleepers rot more rapidly than those on the adjoining embankment and viaduct.

Railway gauges were not at first standardized and various distances between the rails were tried but the one which became dominant in northern England was 4 ft. 8½ in. Despite the efforts of Isambard Brunel to perpetuate a 7-ft. gauge, which he believed would lead to faster and safer running, the narrower gauge became standard, but it was not until 1892 that the last of the broad-gauge track was converted to what is now known as standard gauge. British engineers planned many of the first lines abroad and they,

---

[1] When the Union Pacific line was being constructed across the High Plains in the 1860s each sleeper cost $2.50 (10s.): in 1945 an untreated sleeper in the States cost $1.34 and a treated $2.07.

naturally, adopted the standard British gauge unless local circumstances suggested an alternative. A curious exception to this occurred in Ireland where the gauge of the main lines was fixed at 5 ft. 3 in.; this was due to an absurd averaging of existing gauges. In Russia 5 ft. was adopted and in Spain and India 5 ft. 6 in. While broader gauges can carry more passengers or a heavier load per vehicle they do demand a wider substructure and more gentle curves and so are more expensive to construct. To reduce the cost of construction narrower gauges have been used in countries or areas where traffic was not expected to be heavy. The precise gauge adopted has frequently been a matter of chance: for example, Lord Cromer in 1892 failed to notify the Railway Committee at the Foreign Office that the Sudan Railway was to be laid to 3 ft. 6 in., instead of the previously agreed metre, and so two-thirds of the Uganda line was built before the discrepancy was realized. The Mad River and Lake Erie Railway, the first line west of the Alleghenies, was commenced in 1835 and its gauge of 4 ft. 10 in. was chosen to fit a locomotive purchased in New Jersey and for a time this became the standard gauge for the State of Ohio.

PRINCIPAL GAUGES OF THE WORLD

Ft. In.	Metres	Area
5 6	1·676	Iberia, India and Ceylon, Chile and Argentina
5 3	1·600	Ireland, Brazil, South Australia and Victoria
5 0	1·524	U.S.S.R.
4 8½	1·435	Areas unspecified for other gauges
3 6	1·067	Southern Africa, Congo, Sudan, Nigeria, Gold Coast, South and Western Australia, Queensland, New Zealand, East Indies, Japan, Chile, Ecuador, Central America
3 5¼	1·050	Algeria and Middle East
3 3⅜	1·000	East Africa, French West Africa, India and south-eastern Asia, South America
3 0	0·914	Ireland, Colombia and Central America
2 11	0·891	Some Swedish lines
2 6	0·762	India, Victoria, Sierra Leone
2 5½	0·750	Some lines in Germany and South America
2 0	$\begin{cases} 0·610 \\ 0·600 \end{cases}$	South West Africa, and some lines India and Venezuela

B

It has been found in South Africa that the narrow-gauge capacity can be increased, with abnormal loading-gauge, to meet most of the needs of an expanding economy. It is not the gauge which in itself causes difficulties but the meeting of varying gauges which results in trouble. The problems of variation are experienced in Europe with Russia and Spain, where special wagons, which can be adapted to either gauge, have been used; in Africa plans to link the railways of eastern (metre gauge) and southern (3 ft. 6 in.) systems have been handicapped by the accidental difference of gauge; in India where there is a broad gauge of 5 ft. 6 in. and a network of metre gauge; in the Argentine where the rail reticule in the hinterland of Buenos Aires has gauges of 5 ft. 6 in. and 4 ft. 8½ in.; in Australia where there is a great variety by states. This break at frontiers has led to so many difficulties it is clear that but for the prohibitive cost of conversion Australia would by now have had a standard gauge as recommended by various Commissions.

AUSTRALIAN GAUGES—BY ROUTE MILES

	5' 3"	4' 8½"	3' 6"	2' 6"	2' 0"
Commonwealth Railways	—	1,112	1,088	—	—
N.S.W.*	—	6,113	35	—	—
Queensland	—	84	7,511	—	33
S. Australia	1,594	—	959	—	—
Tasmania*	—	—	722	—	—
Victoria	4,525	—	—	114	—
W. Australia*	—	—	4,385	—	—

A gauge of 2 ft. (600 mm.) is regarded as almost a miniature, yet it was successfully used by the Germans for opening the almost waterless Otavi country behind Swakopmund.

The present dominance of 4 ft. 8½ in. gauge in the U.S.A. was not always so for in 1871 there were 23 different gauges ranging from 3 ft. to 6 ft. In 1885 the Conference of Railroad Presidents decided on uniformity and in twelve months 14,000 track miles were converted. On two successive days in 1886 nearly 7,000 miles of 5-ft. track in the southern states were narrowed. In

* Includes company-owned lines within these states.

recent years there has been a sad decline in the mileage of narrow gauge lines in the U.S.A. In 1879 there were 4,188 miles and now the almost sole survivor is the 3-ft. East Broad Top R.R. which serves semi-anthracitic collieries by carrying their output, in standard gauge wagons placed on adaptors, down to the Pennsylvania R.R.

Railways demand a great organization in the construction, maintenance and operation and in all of these geographical factors can play a part. In succeeding chapters the aim is to show how in different environments railway pattern and operation have been affected by the physical and economic conditions and, at the same time, how the operational features are in a state of transition under the stress of modern conditions.

CHAPTER II

THE RAILWAY MEN

MANY men have played their parts in the evolution of the world's railway pattern and, while this volume is not the place for a comprehensive biography of any one or for exhaustive lists of names, it is appropriate that some recognition should be given to the part various skills have played both in a general way and by individuals. Many are the skills which were used: the surveyor, the engineer, the contractor, the navvy, the financier, the lawyer, the manager and superintendent. There were also the men of vision who proposed railways which "practical" men derided as being impossible, yet later the construction of these lines opened up new territory and resulted in economic expansion.

Some Men of Vision

Thomas Gray wrote *Observations of a General Iron Rail-Way* which, first issued in 1820, had a fifth edition by 1825 and was translated into several European languages. These translations undoubtedly influenced the provision of railways in Belgium and Germany but Gray's views did not find acceptance at home. Gray proposed that there should be six trunk lines radiating from London with branches to towns off the main routes. Sensible as were these proposals they were ahead of their time and, when trunk lines were being considered, a few years later, speculation ruled and there was, by deliberate choice of Parliament, encouragement of rival routes on the plea that they would provide healthy competition.

The brief phrase *Cape to Cairo*, coined by Cecil Rhodes, caught the public fancy when Rhodes commenced his still unfulfilled scheme for the first longitudinal transcontinental railway. Under his enthusiasm the railhead advanced northwards, despite rinderpest destroying the draught cattle, and the last 492 miles to Bulawayo were completed in 500 working days. When Rhodes died the railhead was at Broken Hill and, with no one to replace him as a driving force, extension halted although Alfred Beit had left one and a half million pounds to aid the enterprise.

The United States has been fortunate in having men of imagination. Asa Whitney, a New York merchant, advocated assiduously in many pamphlets a railway from the Great Lakes to the Pacific while the territory between was still unknown. He wished to see a line from Lake Michigan to the mouth of the Columbia River. Theodore D. Judah in the 1850s believed that it was possible to take a line through the mountains. Although he was regarded as a dreamer he was known as *The Railway Pathfinder*, and it was his advocacy which persuaded the Government of the day to support the scheme for a railway from Council Bluffs to San Francisco. In another capacity James T. Hill, under whose organizing and directing genius the Great Northern R.R. was built, was termed *The Empire Builder* because, with vision, he directed his energies to developing the territorial resources of his railway "empire".

Surveyors

In Britain opposition to railways was widespread: a poet laureate could be applauded for writing about a proposed railway to Windermere:

> Is there no nook of English ground secure
> From rash assault? . . .

and it was frequently the surveyor who had to take the brunt of the dislike. George Stephenson was threatened with a ducking if he surveyed the lands of a Captain Bradshaw while pistols were brandished at others. Opposition came from fear of the effects on vested interests such as those of horse-breeders and of hay and grain merchants but it also came from prejudice that it would cause the old ways to disappear.

With the Railway Mania in Britain the demand for surveyors was greater than the supply: classes were advertised by self-appointed teachers and with little or no training "surveyors" were receiving "five guineas a day and all expenses". No wonder errors were found when the plans came to be scrutinized. After the mania careful work again became the standard. These early plans, with their profiles, were drawn to a scale of four inches to a mile. It might have been expected that as they became available Ordnance Survey maps would displace the special survey but they did not because the engineers required more detail than the official maps showed. A detailed knowledge of the ground was required : Robert Stephenson walked twenty times over the route when he was planning the London and Birmingham Railway. Even in Britain physical conditions could be very arduous for the surveyor : when the Settle and Carlisle line was being planned the surveyor was snowed up for weeks at a time on Blea Moor.

Outwith Europe the surveyor was frequently the pioneer of civilization. America saw the railway surveyors in the west not merely mapping the ground for the first time but also exploring it, frequently with vigorous opposition from the Indians, in their attempts to find passable gradients across the western cordillera. The problem was not that of connecting towns, for they were non-existent, but of finding passes and some took long searches. When the Canadian Pacific route was being decided across the mountains the surveyor Walter Moberly had been defeated in finding a route across the Gold Range until an eagle revealed the presence of a gap now known as Eagle Pass. The Rogers, uncle and nephew, followed up most ably the work of Moberly in blazing a trail for the C.P.R. across the Selkirks.

Apart from the exploration required the survey was often dangerous work ; for example in some canyons the surveyors had to be suspended from long ropes to take their readings. As there was no deflection to towns and as construction was to be as cheap as possible the early railways of the west reflected closely in their plan and profile the grain of the country. A Philadelphia engineer Henry Meiggs, adapting the plans of a Cornishman, William Murley, is famous for carrying the lessons learnt in North America further and planning the difficult Oroya line in Peru.

In addition to survey for line alignment with alterations in structures, there is constant work in the correction of railway plans, and the scale of this can be appreciated with four million acres of land owned in the United States alone by railways for transport purposes.

Engineers

The work of the engineer is better known than that of most railway workers and biographies exist of some such as the Stephensons, Brunel, Vignoles and Locke. Spectacular bridges, viaducts and tunnels remain as monuments to the skill of these engineers but it is also seen in the less spectacular lines which, laid out closely in response to the grain of the country and to the demands of traffic, efficiently and economically carry the traffic for which they were designed.

Prince Michael Ivanovitch Khilkoff acted much for Russian railways as did Prince Peter for shipbuilding. The former worked in an engineering shop, then in America as a navvy on the construction of a transcontinental line, served as a fireman and engine-driver and then as a superintendent. He was thus well qualified when, as Russian Minister of Transport, he became responsible for completing the Siberian Railway and helped with the engineering problems of rounding Lake Baikal.

Contractors

Contracting for great works was little understood when railway construction became widespread and in the stress of active work those with a flair became powerful figures in the system. A famous group was that of Peto, Betts and Brassey who made their name in Britain and then, with plant idle, became interested in European contracts. In 1852, having just completed one set of continental contracts, they undertook to construct the railway from Montreal to Hamilton, the first trunk line in Canada. It says much for their resources that they were able to stand a loss on this contract of a million pounds. Contractors of this status acquired their reputations by fair and honest work. Another reputable contractor was Joseph Firbank, who, having worked at the age of seven in a Durham mine, between 1846 and 1886 contracted for various lines in Britain which extended from Carlisle in the north to Bournemouth in the south and from South Wales to Kent. As contractor he was responsible for translating into reality J. S. Crossley's plans for the Settle and Carlisle line.

Some of the less reputable contractors accepted work at prices which they knew could not pay but relied on the *truck system* to make their profit; food and drink were sold to the labourers at inflated prices which made the contractor's profit.

Navvies

The men who constructed the early canals in Britain were termed *navigators*, which term was contracted by 1775 to navvy,[1] and since the earthworks of the railways resembled those of canals the labourers were called the same. Many of the early navvies were *bankers* from the Fenlands but, with the demand exceeding the supply from this source, men came from the uplands of northern England and from Ireland to sell their physical strength. These men were picturesque characters, known on the pay-roll by their colourful nicknames, and they fed their strength by being heavy eaters of beef—18 lb. a week was usual. They wandered about and formed a gang of about twelve and would contract to move so much "dirt". The pay was good but the men were frequently the victims of the truck system and were given miserable sod bothies in which to sleep. When inflamed with drink on pay-days, the various nationalities quarrelled with each other and numerous are the records of riots. For the early Scottish railways is available a detailed story of the Irish immigrants who worked on the lines and the conditions under which they worked.[2]

Some of the English navvies migrated to the continent and helped to construct, for example, the Paris-Rouen line. Most of the labour used on the continent was local. Italians, in particular, have proved able workers and when the St. Gotthard tunnel was being driven they were almost the only men willing to work for low wages under the arduous conditions; over 300 men were killed on this job. Italians were taken to South West Africa to construct the Otavi line in from Swakopmund but when they repeatedly struck work for higher wages the local Hereros people, who proved excellent workers, were induced to cease fighting the Germans and become railway builders. In constructing the pioneer lines of North America the labour had to be organized like an army. When in the summer of 1887

[1] This was spelt *navy* until *The Times* in 1846 introduced the present spelling.
[2] J. E. Handley. *The Irish in Scotland, 1798–1845*. Cork, 1943, p. 60, *et seq.*

10,000 men and 3,500 teams were engaged in the construction of 545 miles in Dakota and Montana all supplies were hauled from the base to the front at railhead. At a railhead which acted as a base while a fresh assault was being prepared a temporary town, known as *Hell-on-wheels*, sprang up almost overnight and from these halt points in the building of the Union Pacific R.R. cities such as North Platte, Cheyenne and Laramie date. Frequently the navvies became imbued with the spirit of rivalry and fought an opposing railway construction unit. This might be a literal fight such as occurred when the Hill and Harriman concerns were each trying to build a track across Oregon alongside the Columbia river. Sometimes it just developed as a trial of strength to see which unit could build most rapidly. During the advance west from Omaha 2,000 men were engaged in grading the route and 1,500 were cutting sleepers in addition to those actually laying the track. These labourers were harassed by the attacks of the Red Indians, especially the Cheyennes and Sioux, until General Grant succeeded in getting a treaty of peace. Despite the adverse conditions and the lure of the gold workings, which caused many to desert, in 1866 245 miles were laid in 182 working days.

The Chinese have proved to be some of the best railway construction workers and they helped to build the Union Pacific, Canadian Pacific and Siberian lines. When the C.P.R. in 1882 was wrestling with the massive works through British Columbia they could obtain only broken-down white labour and so, despite local protests, the company brought in 2,000 Chinese and it was by their energy that Craigellachie was reached as early as 1885 and thus the Confederation of Canada was linked into an entity.

South America with the rarefied air of the high Andes proved difficult to labour in and it was found when the Transandine line was being built that the Chilean *peon* was best able to stand the conditions. One unusual qualification for a labour force was seen during the extension, before World War I, of the line from Medina Saleh to Mecca when all the men had to be Mahomedans. As the construction gangs worked south from Damascus they were attacked by Bedouin until a strong force of Turkish troops inflicted a heavy defeat.

Labour problems have been solved in various ways. During

the construction of the Siberian line criminals and exiles, under military guards, were employed. Prisoners have also been employed in recent years; in 1941 some 20,000 prisoners were employed in arid heat to lay a section of the Trans-Sahara line for the Vichy Government, while on the notorious *Railway of Death* from Thailand to Burma the Japanese used some 60,000 prisoners of whom 13,300 perished.[1] Since the war volunteer youth brigades in Yugoslavia have constructed lines the first of which to be completed was that in 1947 from Samac to Sarajevo. Labour supply has become a problem and steam and diesel power have been adopted to work machines and it has been claimed that a steam shovel can do the work of 500 men. One device to move great masses of gravel is to use high-pressure jets of water with temporary conduits to where the material is deposited to form an embankment. Another powerful weapon is the dragline excavator. Even so in countries such as India, with very low wages it was found cheaper to use local labour with primitive tools rather than to adopt modern machinery with expensive technicians. A track-laying machine can lay about four and a half miles of single track in a day yet when laying the Rhodesian section of the Cape-to-Cairo line native labourers, without any massive equipment, laid five and three-quarter miles in a working day. In the industrial countries where labour is at a premium machinery is being used more and more to lay and to renovate track.

Financiers

Until 1843 British railway schemes were financed by orthodox methods but for a period after that the normal was forgotten in the fever-heat of speculation. Capital was available, the Bank Rate was two and a half per cent and companies such as the London and Birmingham were paying 10 per cent. Speculators were quick to see their opportunity to create attractive bubble schemes. Some of the investors were men of straw: for example, the son of a charwoman sent in his name as a subscriber for £52,000 of stock in the London and York Railway Company although his weekly wage as a clerk was only twelve shillings. A Parliamentary

[1] It is estimated that 150,000 Asiatic coolies also lost their lives in constructing the 240 miles of this line. *See* C. A. Fisher, "The Thailand-Burma Railway", *Econ. Geogy.*, xxiii, 1947, pp. 85–97.

Return was called for as to subscribers and the contemporary *Annual Register* commented:

> "The juxtaposition of names and descriptions offers some remarkable contrasts, the same column presenting peers and printers, vicars and vice-admirals, spinsters and half-pays, M.P.s and special pleaders, professors and cotton spinners, gentlemen's cooks and Queen's Counsels, attorneys' clerks and college scouts, waiters at Lloyd's, relieving officers and excisemen, barristers and butchers, Catholic priests and coachmen, editors and engineers, dairymen and dyers, braziers and bankers, beersellers, butlers, domestic servants, footmen, and mailguards, with a multitude of other callings unrecorded in the book of trades."[1]

One financial genius of the period, although his methods were not acceptable, was George Hudson. This man was a linen draper in York and from the 'thirties he became interested in railways. His ability, financial astuteness and vigour resulted in his obtaining control of various companies and in two days he persuaded shareholders of three companies to submit to Parliament Bills which would cost £10 million to execute if the Acts were obtained. Hudson was known as the *Railway King* and was almost deified until it was realized that capital was being used to pay dividends. In 1849 he was deposed but he left behind lines which were in a sounder physical state than when he obtained control and he had created one of the greatest railway companies of England—the Midland Railway. Great sums of money were wiled out of the pockets of the British public for foreign as well as home lines. By 1881, when 18,175 miles of line were open to traffic in Britain, some £831 million had been spent and the shareholders were apprehensive that the capital account could not be closed because it was found that constant expenditure had to be incurred, as it still has, to meet the changing demands of traffic.

In North America the great financiers included Cornelius Vanderbilt, David H. M. Moffatt and Henry M. Flagler. In the United States the capital stock, which gave the voting power control, could be small and the mortgage bonds which supplied

[1] F. McDermott, *Life and Work of Joseph Firbank*. London, 1887, p. 20.

the real sinews of war large (unlike Britain where borrowing powers were limited to one-third of the stock), and this opened the way to financial skulduggery. Even in 1946 in the U.S.A. for each mile of line open stock was issued, on an average, for $31,485 and bonds for $40,734, so the owners of the greater part of the capital, although secured by property, have no control over policy. Many of the financiers were men of integrity but some were just stockjobbers who were indifferent to the welfare of the public utility which they controlled: Daniel Webster, James Fisk and Jay Gould in the 1870s put the Erie R.R. into such financial straits that it was inefficient for years. Cornelius Vanderbilt in 1863 commenced purchasing in a large way the hitherto unprofitable Harlem R.R. stock and so improved the management of this company that it paid dividends; he then acquired control of the Hudson River R.R. and New York Central companies but was defeated in his attempt to gain control of the Erie. Vanderbilt developed the companies he controlled so that they became useful and profitable lines.

Some American lines can be regarded as the child of one man and frequently represent bold thinking. Moffatt, who was known as the *Silver King* from his mining interests, financed the railway which pushes westwards from Denver on its way to the Pacific and tunnels the continental divide under Rollins Pass. This was one of the few American lines which from its inception was aligned to the highest standards of engineering and was a rival in its constructional feats to the great Alpine railways. Henry M. Flagler, an oil capitalist, extended the Florida East Coast Railway, which he had bought in 1885, from Miami across the Florida Keys to Key West: this work, originally nicknamed *Flagler's Folly*, was completed in 1912 and operated until 1935 when it was seriously damaged by a hurricane. It never played a real part in the traffic with Cuba as had been hoped.

Not always was it possible to obtain from the public the capital required and so various governments, lacking large funds from taxation, gave liberal land grants which could be sold by the company and so encourage settlement. The first U.S. company to receive a land grant was the Illinois Central which was granted over two and a half million acres in return for building 705 miles of line within six years. The policy has been adopted many times since : for example, for the transcontinental Union and Central Pacific lines, the C.P.R. and the early lines in New South Wales. Federal grants of land, with which eight per cent of the U.S. mileage was constructed, were in favour during the period 1850–71. In return for the land grants the railways, until there was a repealing Act in 1945, carried all Government material, including mails, at half rate, and it was estimated that nine and a half times the value of the land at the time it was granted had been returned to the Government while the Illinois Central had paid $60 million in Special State Taxes for land originally valued at $3¼ million. Land grants still retained have greatly helped the companies because of the royalties payable on exploitation of their oil reserves.

In the struggle to obtain money to construct the C.P.R. Donald A. Smith (Lord Strathcona), aided by his cousin, George Stephen, wrestled successfully with public opinion and obtained grants from the Government. For the rival line to the west, that from Winnipeg to Prince Rupert, the Government guaranteed interest on bonds.

There has been a widening in the ownership of railway stock in America as the following examples reveal :

NUMBER OF HOLDERS OF STOCK

Company		1904	1918	1945
Chesapeake and Ohio	...	1,478	7,220	82,329
New York Central ...	...	11,781	31,767	59,495
Northern Pacific ...	...	368	27,338	25,129
Pennsylvania ...	...	44,175	110,765	214,995
Union Pacific ...	...	14,256	36,953	56,691

The par value of the railway stock and bonds represents almost one-fifth of the whole company securities listed in the Stock Exchanges of the U.S.A.

Lawyers

Railway schemes have been responsible for many legal battles, particularly in countries such as Britain where there were vested interests anxious to prevent the construction. Parliament arranged that schemes should be examined by Select Committees of both

Houses in order to save the time of most members and the appearance of the promoters before these committees, with their legal advisers, led to impressive battles of words. Illustrative of the forensic enquiry are these short extracts from the 772 folio pages which record the examination by the House of Commons Committee into the 1825 Bill for the Liverpool and Manchester Railroad. Questions asked of George Stephenson included :

Q. What is the general average rate at which they draw goods over those Railroads ?

A. Not more than six to seven miles an hour, at some they may pass at the rate of seven miles an hour [p. 209].

Q. Stone blocks for the purpose of founding the Railway upon, at the rate of 1s. 4d. each, amounting to 15,557 £ is that sufficient ?

A. Yes.

Q. Chairs or pedestals—for what purpose are they provided ? What are they ?

A. They are of cast iron, and placed upon the stone blocks to receive the rails [p. 219].

Having dealt with the witnesses Counsel then summed up, and Mr. Adam, for the Bill, rightly said of the proposal "Let my learned Friends disguise this matter as they please, your determination will be to postpone the application of steam to the conveyance of goods from one part of the kingdom to the other, and to prevent its advance with that rapidity which is necessary, to keep pace with the other applications of this powerful agency" [p. 741]. At the end of the 38 days' enquiry the Committee reported against the Bill and so, for the time being, the opposition had won.

Such legal battles were very expensive and, the cost being charged to capital if the Bill were passed, it became a permanent liability on the dividend capacity of the company. As an indication of the severity of the burden may be instanced the £14,414 per mile cost of the Blackwall Railway Act and £5,190 per mile for that of the Manchester and Birmingham line. During periods of activity Counsel received up to £300 a day : Charles Austin was said to have averaged £40,000 a year for four years in the 'forties. While the cost might be high it was accepted as inevitable by the promoters for the forensic skill might make all the difference to a scheme receiving Parliamentary sanction.

Legal influence also came in over the creation of larger companies from the fusion of those of local interest. Amalgamation in Britain required Parliamentary sanction and was the subject of a Royal Commission in 1872. It was not unknown for permission to be refused at one application, on the argument that competition would be stifled, and to be granted at the next.

In addition to the part lawyers played in forming the companies their services were required as specialists in the interpretation of carrier-law as it affected railways. The volume *The Law of Railways applicable to Scotland* by Deas and Ferguson runs to over a thousand pages (1897 edition) and it reveals how necessary the companies found the services of lawyers in the day-to-day business.

Managers

In Britain the railway network evolved from a colliery wagonway and it gradually acquired a complex organization to control both the actual operation and the man-power. The early railways were small affairs over which a General Manager could exercise a patriarchal, and sometimes dictatorial, control. Every man on the line and every manufacturer would be known personally and success depended upon the skill with which the General Manager responded to the demands for transport. In the nineteenth century Britain was fortunate in the men who were selected by the directors to act as managers. Their names became identified with the company they served and it was by their acumen and foresight that advances were made—George Findlay (L.N.W.R.), James Allport (M.R.), James Walker (N.B.R.) are but three of many. Sometimes the Secretary of the company and sometimes the Chairman of the Directors loomed greater than the Manager as leader of commercial policy but if there was a group of outstanding ability the company could be as powerful as a small kingdom: the history of the L.N.W.R. in the 'eighties when it was under the powerful chairmanship of Sir Richard Moon and under the executive guidance of Sir George Findlay, ably assisted by the Superintendent of the Line, George P. Neele, shows how much individuals evolved the fortunes of a company.

Other companies and other countries can show parallel cases of collaboration between an inspirer and an executive of policy. In the United States Thomas A. Scott was selected as a clerk by J. Edgar Thomson and when the former became chief executive under the latter as President of the Pennsylvania R.R. the company entered its period of expansion.

Man-power

In the nineteenth century railways had little difficulty in attracting labour although the hours worked were long and the paucity of mechanical aids made the work arduous.[1] With the general rising of standards of living and the discrepancy between the cost of living and wages which companies or nationalized boards feel able to pay with dwindling traffic, there is a shortage of staff. This problem is being tackled by introducing modern equipment and by scrapping little-used lines. Between 1938 and 1953 on the Netherlands Railway, with faster trains and fewer steam locomotives, it has been found possible to use 25 per cent less driving personnel per 1,000 train-miles.

Long-distance trains may demand special facilities which add to the operating cost: corridors through the tender were provided for the non-stop run King's Cross to Waverley, rest-cars for the relief crew on the 500-mile run, without an intermediate town, between Mafeking and Bulawayo, while in a number of countries dormitories are provided for men obliged to sleep away from home owing to the duty-roster. Again there is usually a mileage payment and in the United States for freight trains a 100-miles or eight hours' running (for passenger trains five hours) counts as a day's work and a bonus is paid for any excess mileage or hours: this has reduced some of the financial advantage of diesel-electric working.

Both craft and general unions exist among the railway workers and inter-union strife has been added to dissatisfaction with working conditions and strikes, which have effects rapidly

[1] Robert Eton's novel, *The Faithful Years*, gives a good idea of the attraction railway work had for many men.

apparent to the rest of the community, have occurred at various periods in most countries.

To house workers in isolated areas the railway organizations have constructed many houses and in the larger railway centres, such as Crewe, the town is dominated by the railway employees. When the G.W.R. selected Swindon as the centre for their locomotive works a cottage estate was built, using stone quarried from the Box Tunnel, and by 1846, when the first locomotive was completed, the population of the town was nearly 5,000 of whom nearly one-seventh were employed in the works.

CHAPTER III

THE LAND AND THE RAIL

NOWADAYS it is difficult to realize the physical obstacles against which the railway pioneers pressed with what would now be regarded as inadequate equipment.

"There were difficulties from end to end: from high and steep mountains; from snows; from deserts where there was a scarcity of water, and from gorges and flats where there was an excess; difficulties from cold and heat; from a scarcity of timber and from obstructions of rock; difficulties in keeping a large force on a long line; from Indians; and from want of labour."[1]

Many of these conditions were due to the physical environment and perhaps the group which can still be appreciated are those relating to the landscape although, even in this group, it is sometimes difficult to visualize the former appearance after a century of agriculture and mining.

When a railway is being laid down on the map two main considerations prevail—to join important places in the shortest rail distance and to avoid undue expenditure on engineering works. The balance between these two dictates the route which is selected. In industrial countries, such as Britain, expenditure per mile was much greater than could have been contemplated by a young nation, such as the nineteenth-century United States, and so in the Old World the modifications to the landscape were greater. Many examples may be drawn from the earlier lines as to the immense quantities of earthworks which were shifted. Roscoe, in his guide to the first of the trunk lines completed, computed that the earth and rock shifted between London and Birmingham and the height to which they were lifted demanded an expenditure

[1] C. P. Huntington's address to U.S. Congress, quoted by F. A. Talbot, *Railway Conquest of the World*. London, 1911, p. 59.

of energy half as much again as that used in constructing the Great Pyramid.

A statement as to the physical alteration to the landscape was made on completion of the G.C.R. main line from near Staveley (Derbyshire) to Quainton Road (Buckinghamshire). For the 106 miles of this, the last trunk line in Britain, 15 acres of land were used to each mile of route and from this land 13·82 million cu. yds. of earth and rock were excavated and on it laid 0·22 million cu. yds. of concrete, about three times that volume of brickwork and 9,000 cu. yds. of ashlar masonry, while to finish the permanent way 1·12 million cu. yds. of ballast were deposited. The quantity of earthworks excavated per mile was 130,219 cu. yds. and while this was probably above the average per mile of double track in Britain it does help to give some idea of the vast scale of alterations made along the main British railway routes.[1] On the Norwegian line from Bergen to Voss the excavations meant the removal of $1\frac{1}{4}$ million cu. yds. of earth and the blasting away of over a million cu. yds. of rock. For other lines similar figures could be given but even without statistics it is clear that the engineers and contractors had to be masters of logistics.

Gradients

It was argued by great railway engineers, such as the Stephensons, that a railway should be as level as possible whereas others thought that an undulating profile would be as cheap to operate with impetus on the descents making up for increased fuel-consumption on the ascents. By dint of heavy works many of the great trunk lines of England were laid as flat as possible. When capital was short then the works could not be so elaborate : an example of this was the M.R. extension from Leicester to Bedford which was constructed during the Crimean War and, without adequate finances, the route included the Desborough Bank with four miles of 1 in 50.[2] Later the company avoided this incubus by a deviation line with better gradients. Severe gradients cannot

---

[1] Based on R. L. Sherlock, *Man as a geological agent*. London, 1922.

[2] In Britain a gradient is expressed as 1 in 50—i.e. 1 ft. rise for 50 ft. along whereas in some other countries it is expressed as a percentage, e.g. 1 in 20 is 5 per cent, 1 in 100 is 1 per cent.

always be avoided and an example of this is the notorious Lickey Incline on the Birmingham and Bristol line of the former M.R. This section was so difficult to operate that for long special banking locomotives were provided and the only British locomotive with ten coupled wheels, to secure great adhesion, was built to work this bank. Descent can raise problems and on Field Hill section of the C.P.R. across the Rockies, now by-passed, the brakes slivered steel off the rails and safety trap points had to be installed.

Where very steep gradients cannot be avoided it is necessary to supplement the adhesion of the locomotives by either a rack rail or by a central rail which is gripped (Fell system) or by cable haulage. By using the rack rail, on which driving pinions engage, gradients as steep as 1 in 3 have been attempted, for example on the Pilatus mountain line near Lucerne. The Manitou and Pike's Peak Railway, worked by Abt rack, climbs 7,549 ft. in 8·9 miles to 14,109 ft. above sea-level with a maximum gradient of 1 in 4 whereas the adhesion-worked California Western R.R. between Shake City and Summit, $1\frac{1}{2}$ miles apart, had to curve for $8\frac{1}{2}$ miles to climb 1,180 ft. with a maximum gradient of 1 in 33. The Fell system was used between 1868 and 1871 to work a temporary summer service over the Mont Cenis Pass while the tunnel was being bored. The track was then shipped to Rio de Janeiro and for a number of years used on a line ascending the edge of the Brazilian plateau; it has now been converted to adhesion working. The Rimutaka Incline in New Zealand, with a gradient of 1 in 15, is worked on the Fell system.

APPROXIMATE GRADIENT LIMITS FOR WORKING

1 in $1\frac{1}{8}$ ...	...	Telpher
1 in 2 ...	...	Funicular-cable
1 in 8 ...	...	Rack, single coach
1 in 14 ...	...	Limit of adhesion working
1 in 70 ...	...	Limit for express working

Steep sections have sometimes been worked by inclined planes with the descending vehicles balancing, at the other end of a cable, the ascending: the original line inland from Santos had such a system but it proved a serious bottleneck for only four sets of vehicles could pass in an hour. The public did not only suffer in the time of the journey but also in cost for the company were allowed to charge as for 6·87 miles extra on this five miles of expensive working.

To overcome the gradient drop of 1,552 ft. on the eastern scarp of the African Rift Valley a rope "lift" was installed, with gradients varying from 1 in 7 to 1 in 1¾, but an improved alignment was opened in 1901 and yet a third in 1948. Up the grade in use from 1901–48 trains required two hours to cover 15 miles and although this was much faster than the original alignment it became an incubus with the increased demands of traffic.

For still steeper gradients the use of rails is abandoned and telpher cableways have become popular in areas such as Switzerland as they avoid the need to bridge cross-ravines and well-known examples are that to the summit of Säntis (8,215 ft.) and the daring 1,155 ft.-high span of the Kandersteg–Stock telpher.

Curves

Curves are a way of avoiding obstacles and it was long thought in Britain that curves sharper than a mile in radius were dangerous and offered excessive resistance to trains. While this view was modified nevertheless sharp curves have frequently been eased because of their drawbacks. Speed restrictions are made because of the sharpness of a curve, for example at Inverkeithing (north of the Forth Bridge) with a radius of 1,188 ft.[1] speed has to be reduced to 25 m.p.h. although for southbound trains it would be desirable to be travelling fast with a long bank of 1 in 70 ahead.

Lines curving, and gradually ascending, can cross mountainous country without tunnel construction and this type of alignment was freely adopted in pioneer areas. In Asia the Kalka-Simla

[1] In Britain curves are measured by the radius but in the U.S. they are given in degrees (the angle between two lines drawn from the centre of the circle to the ends of a 100-ft. segment of the circle). On mountainous lines curves of 11° are encountered and on the Uintah Railway in Colorado (abandoned in 1938) there were curves of 66°. A curve of 10 chains (660 ft.) is 8·68° and a 10° curve has a radius of 573 ft. In the case of the Inverkeithing curve full super-elevation cannot be given because of diverging tracks—hence the severity of the speed limit.

Railway ascends 4,700 ft. with almost continuous curves; these curves are so sharp that the locomotives and short carriages overhang the track. On the Darjeeling Railway, which is of 2 ft. gauge, the line spirals to climb without a gradient steeper than 1 in 23; at Agony Point the curve has a radius of only 70 ft. and there is a spectacular figure-of-eight loop. Not all curves are due to high relief for water bodies may also deflect the route and the longest continuous curve in the U.S. is that of $9\frac{1}{2}$ miles along the western shore of Lake Pontachartrain, near New Orleans.

Straight stretches of line do exist: the longest in the world is across the Nullabor plain in Australia, 309 miles, while that in the U.S., between Wilmington and Hamlet (N.Ca.), is 78·8 miles without a curve. These mileages make the longest British section between Hull and Selby, 18 miles, seem very slight. Most of the straight stretches are in lowland but that of the Denver and Rio Grande Western R.R. between Villa Grove and Alamosa (Col.), 52·8 miles long, is unique in that it is 7,000 ft. above sea-level and surrounded by rugged ranges.

Geological influences

The geological outcrop may greatly influence the profile of a line as is seen from Fig. 1, where despite heavy excavation in the Tring area, with a cutting nearly $2\frac{1}{2}$ miles long and an average depth of 40 ft., there is a long ascent at 1 in 335 on the dip-slope of the chalk, and on the scarp edge the gradient has been reduced by building an embankment ramp from the cutting end down to the Gault lowland. The volume of chalk removed from the cutting was only kept down to $1\frac{1}{2}$ million cu. yds. because the sides could be left steep and still stand weathering.

The railway engineers have to be on their guard against apparently favourable geomorphological conditions. When the German engineers were constructing the line in from Dar-es-Salaam they used the Mukondokwa valley and at Kidete ran the line along the axis of an alluvial fan formed by a side stream. In 1930 the wet-season lake burst through the fan which dammed it but fortunately the railway had been previously re-aligned on the flanks of the main valley.

Tunnels are also affected by the nature of the rocks through which they are cut: it may not be necessary to line some rocks whereas with quicksand the brick lining may have to be over two feet thick. Mobile London Clay has caused trouble in tunnels both in the excavation and in preparing the lining and it was only with the invention of the Greathead shield, and its improved form the Price rotary excavator, which pierced the clay and allowed iron segments to be bolted into position before the clay

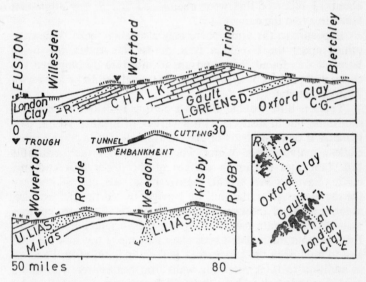

FIG. 1. INFLUENCE OF GEOLOGY—LONDON TO RUGBY

The inset locates the line from Euston (E) to Rugby (R) with land over 500 ft. in black. On the section the "strong" formations have names in capitals and the less resistant in lower case (R. = Reading Beds, C. = Cornbrash, G. = Great Oolite). The resistant materials are associated with tunnels and cuttings, while embankments are mainly associated with the less resistant material. *See also* S. H. Beaver, *Geography*, Dec. 1936.

was long exposed, which allowed the London tube railways to be made. With the latest form of shield the working face can be advanced 25 ft. a day. Apparently solid rocks can press in and during the boring of the Simplon tunnel it was found that until the masonry lining was strengthened with steel it could not resist the pressure. The lining in a tunnel is not the arch which shows but a ring extending under the track as well in order to resist rock pressure. In tunnelling there is the danger of running into a "pipe" of unconsolidated material and of tapping a reservoir of water. Such pipes of gravel were found in tunnelling the chalk round London. When the Lötschberg tunnel was being bored the men tapped a fissure filled with glacial deposits and water. It was found impossible either to seal this off or to drain it and so about $1\frac{2}{3}$ miles of line were abandoned and a new alignment taken to avoid the danger area.

Exposure to the atmosphere may also alter rocks. When the tunnel under the Uspallata Pass, across the Andes, was being bored it was found that exposure to moisture decomposed the shales and pockets of gypsum and the tunnel had to be lined with 20 in. of concrete.

There is little trouble where a cutting is made in a massive sandstone but in districts with a variety of inclined strata, particularly if there are beds of clays and marls, cuttings may cause endless maintenance. Water working through the permeable beds lubricates the upper surface of the impervious and, the cutting having given a void, the overlying beds may slide down the dip slope under the pull of gravity. In North Staffordshire, along the line of railways abandoned twenty years ago, cuttings made in such strata have already lost their original cross-profile. Even without intercalated beds clays may move towards the void and to hold open the Haverstock Hill cutting, out of St. Pancras, in addition to thick retaining walls iron beams were run like a roof over the track to keep the walls from moving inwards under the pressure of the London Clay. Another site in this clay where many slips have occurred is New Cross cutting where periodically for over a hundred years the sides have moved.[1] When the Dove Holes cutting slipped during the wet year of 1872 the engineers provided strong side walls and roofed it in to prevent a recurrence of the catastrophe.

Frequently it is the presence of water in the sides of the cutting which leads to slips and then elaborate drainage channels are provided. With masonry structures lime is liable to be drawn by the ground water from the mortar and deposited in the drainage channels and thus close the exit for the water. A few years

[1] For a study of the mechanics of the clay movement see W. H. Ward "Stability of natural slopes", *Geog. Journ.*, May–June, 1945, pp. 170–97.

ago this led to the collapse of a retaining wall at Greenock and the remedy has been to provide weep-holes so aligned that they can be scraped of lime incrustation by running in iron rods. Saturated ground can flow freely and mud-slides are particularly liable after the ground has been heavily frozen because the melt-water lubricates the particles and the material can flow like water down a slope.

In areas with steep slopes the narrow ledge of the railway track is liable to damage from falling stones which have been prised off by sub-aerial weathering. Frost can act freely on some rocks and from the nearly perpendicular sides of the Merstham cutting, where the line to Brighton crosses the chalk of the North Downs, fractured blocks fall. On the line from Wicklow to Bray sections of the track, where it rounded Bray Head, were roofed over, and long walls were erected to prevent scree moving. Another stretch of line in Britain liable to rock falls is the Oban line through the Pass of Brander on the slopes of Cruachan. To minimize damage to trains a high wire fence, with warning wires signalling electrically to a signal-box if they are snapped by a fallen boulder, has been placed on the uphill side.[1] The danger is a real one : in 1946 falling boulders knocked a locomotive off the line in this section.

On the Peruvian Central line scree slides are particularly troublesome. One of the most troublesome sites in the world is at Ocatara, 62 miles from Lima, where the line runs on a shelf cut across a great fan of debris which has descended 3,000 ft. in stone avalanches from a zone where erosion is active on a fantastic scale : here upturned strata are rapidly eroded by frost and the scree movement is accelerated by earthquakes. It was thought that the cutting of a ledge for the railway had produced instability of the scree slope but it is clear that the falls would occur in any case although it is true the vibration of a passing train may disturb boulders temporarily at rest. Falls are most frequent during the wet season, and a bulldozer clears the boulders off the track each morning before a train is allowed to pass. In 1927 a retaining wall was built to try to make falling blocks, which may weigh 50 tons, leap the track but it has not been entirely successful and it is now proposed that the most vulnerable

[1] This device is known in the U.S.A. as a "slide detector fence".

section be roofed with thick reinforced concrete. It is essential for the working of the mines that the supply of oil is maintained and so since 1950 there has been a four-inch pipeline buried in the scree and pumping plant installed to move the oil across the scree section when the oil-wagons cannot pass.

Earth movements may wreck railway structures and to reduce possible damage the new station at Wellington (N.Z.) has special foundations and a jointed steel framework to take up movement : similar protection has been afforded to buildings in Japan since the great Tokyo earthquake of 1923.

High land

High land offers a challenge to the surveyor and engineer and a route with low summits and a line of approach with workable gradients is sought. Abnormally steep gradients may be adopted as an interim measure : when the Kingwood tunnel was being bored for the Baltimore and Ohio R.R. a temporary surface line with a gradient of 1 in 10 was used on which 25-ton locomotives hauled a 15-ton car. On the line from Halberstadt to Blankenberg in the Harz Mountains the engineers could not get better than 1 in 16 and on this section powerful 110-ton locomotives were used but they could only pull their own weight at 10 m.p.h. For main lines such a steep gradient is intolerable and to avoid it the line may zig-zag, or it may swing with great horseshoe or spiral curves to gain height more gradually or it may tunnel to lower the summit.

The interesting American zig-zag device to ascend steep slopes was first adopted in the 1840s to carry coal wagons down into the Nesquehoning valley of Pennsylvania. Train direction is reversed at each angle of the zig-zag and so movement is slow. The technique was adopted for the line using the Rimac valley of Peru when an ascent of 15,693 ft. had to be made between Callao and Galera tunnel : to keep the gradient no steeper than 1 in 25, in a distance of 70 miles, there had to be thirteen of these reversing points as well as horseshoe curves. When the line was being taken across the Blue Mountains in New South Wales zig-zags were provided at Penrith and Lithgow but were eliminated when the flow of traffic justified capital expenditure on tunnels.

All degrees of sharpness of the horseshoe curve are found and one of the best known for its spectacular appearance is that on the Pennsylvania R.R. route to surmount the Allegheny Front west of Altoona. The swings of the line to gain height more gradually may be so great that the line does not appear to the traveller as a horseshoe and an extreme case of such lengthening is the line between La Guaira and Caracas in Venezuela where, although the places are only seven miles apart, the line is 23 miles long to overcome an elevation difference of about 3,000 ft.

Zig-zags can be laid out on one flank of a mountain whereas the horseshoe curve alignment demands an open valley both sides of which are used. Occasionally a line is taken up the one flank of a mountain by providing spiral tunnels, which reverse the direction of a train across the mountainside within the mountain itself and this expensive technique is only warranted where valuable traffic has to pass.

As engineers gained more experience so they became bolder in ascending and there are now five railway summits, all in the Andes, of over 15,000 ft. and worked by normal adhesion loco-motives : by contrast, the highest point in North America reached by a railway is 14,109 ft., the Manitou and Pike's Peak (rack railway), in Europe 11,340 ft., the Jungfrau rack line, in Africa the summit 9,136 ft. of the Kenya and Uganda line and in Britain, for a normal railway, 1,485 ft. between Dalnaspidal and Dal-whinnie on the line which connects Perth and Inverness.

Since the days of canal construction British engineers have been able to persuade shareholders to expend vast sums on the construction of tunnels and thus, although there are no vast mountains, there are in Britain 58 tunnels a mile or more in length and it is interesting to note that most of these are not in the mountainous parts of Scotland or Wales but in the com-paratively low uplands separating the populated districts. An important exception to this is the longest of all—the Severn tunnel (*see* p. 55). The early date of so many British tunnels shows the boldness of the pioneers particularly in tackling the obstacle of the Pennines which separates the traffic-producing centres of Lancashire and Yorkshire. If the location of the tunnels be examined it is also seen how a number could have been avoided if there had not been rivalry over the provision of alternative routes between populated districts. The tunnels of urban railways are referred to on p. 165.

MAJOR TUNNELS ON BRITISH RAILWAYS

Former Company	Tunnel	Between	Length yds.	Hills crossed	Principal Geological Formations
G.W.R.	Severn	Bristol–Newport	7,668	—	Trias and Carboniferous
M.R.	Totley	Sheffield–Manchester	6,230	Pennines	Coal Measures and Millstone Grit
L.N.W.R.	Standedge	Leeds–Manchester	5,340	Pennines	Millstone Grit
G.C.R.	Woodhead No. 1	Sheffield–Manchester	5,297	Pennines	Millstone Grit
"	No. 2	"		"	"
B.R.	No. 3	"		"	"
G.W.R.	Sodbury	Swindon–Newport	4,433	Cotswolds	Oolite
M.R.	Disley	Sheffield–Manchester	3,866	Pennines	Coal Measures
N.E.R.	Bramhope	Leeds–Harrogate	3,754	Pennine spur	Millstone Grit
L.N.W.R.	Ffestiniog	Bettws–Blaenau–Ffestiniog	3,726	Snowdonia	Silurian and intrusions
M.R.	Cowburn	Sheffield–Manchester	3,702	Pennines	Yoredale Series and Carboniferous Limestone
S.E.R.	Sevenoaks	Sevenoaks–Tonbridge	3,451	Scarp ridge	Greensand
G.W.R.	Rhondda	Merthyr Tydfil–Aberdare	3,443	Inter-valley ridge	Lwr. Coal Measures
L.N.W.R.	Morley	Leeds–Manchester	3,350	Pennines	Millstone Grit
G.W.R.	Box	Swindon–Bath	3,212	Cotswolds	Oolite
G.C.R.	Catesby	Brackley–Rugby	2,997	Northampton Uplands	Lias
M.R.	Dove Holes	Derby–Manchester	2,984	Pennines	Millstone Grit and Carboniferous Limestone
L. & Y.R.	Littleborough	Leeds–Manchester	2,885	Pennines	Millstone Grit

On the continent of Europe are many great examples of tunnel construction and, owing to the height of the mountains through which they are bored, the tunnels required associated approach lines which demanded as much skill as the location of the tunnel itself. Most of the mightiest of the tunnels are located in the recent fold mountains : the Alps, the Pyrenees and the Apennines have all been tackled by the railway engineer. One of the most impressive routes is that of the St. Gotthard. The line follows the Reuss valley with an ascending gradient of about 1 in 40 for 18 miles and, to keep the gradient within workable limits, the line spirals in tunnels cut in the flanks of the Reuss valley. The ascent from the south is equally impressive for in addition to spiral tunnels near Giornica the line ascends 2,800 ft. in the 24 miles between Biasca and Airolo. In the 105½ miles of route between Lucerne and Bellinzona is an aggregate tunnelling of 28½ miles while, to pass over cross ravines and minor valleys, are 234 bridges and viaducts. The cost of these works was justified for it reduced the travelling time between Germany and Italy by 36 hours. So rapidly was the route adopted for traffic that within four years of the opening in 1882 the approach lines had to be doubled; there was already a double track through the tunnel.

Pierre Brunner[1] examined the atmospheric conditions in the Alpine tunnels and found that in those over 2¼ miles long the air was warmer throughout the year than it was in the open air whereas in shorter tunnels it was only warmer in the winter. When the St. Gotthard was first bored the maximum rock temperature was 88°F. but it has since fallen to 61°F. A strong current of air flows through a tunnel only if its axis continues that of the valleys, hence the poor movement of air in the Kara-wanken tunnel, which is at right angles to the valleys of Sava and Drava. A difference of height of the portals or of the air pressure between the two ends usually induces a strong current but in the Mont Cenis tunnel, although there is a chimney effect through the difference of height of 456 ft. between the portals, the air movement is weak because it opposes the normal flow of air from the Savoy to Piedmont. When steam was used for traction the natural ventilation often had to be supplemented by fans;

[1] *Der Schweizer Geograph*, 1937.

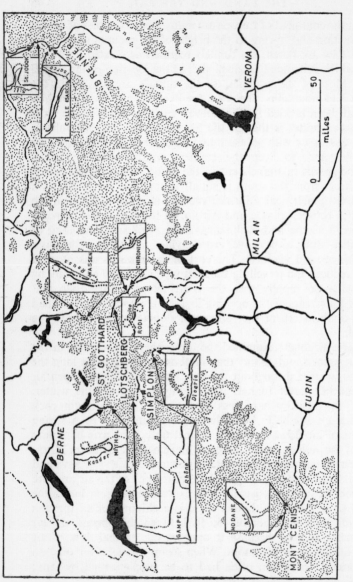

FIG. 2. CROSSING MOUNTAINS—THE ALPS

The railway routes across the Alps are shown with insets, × 10 scale, of the sections of difficult relief where tunnels, (dotted lines) spirals and long loops required to keep the grade within working limits. Lakes in black.

GREAT EUROPEAN TUNNELS

Tunnel	Year opened	Between	Length m.	Length yds.	Years to construct	Electric traction introduced
Simplon	1905	Brigue (Switzerland)–Iselle (Italy)	12	560	6½	1906
Apennine	1934	Florence–Bologna direct line	11	879	10	1934
Gotthard	1882	Göschenen–Airolo	9	547	8¼	1920
Lötschberg	1913	Kandersteg–Goppenstein	9	132	4½	1913
Mont Cenis	1871	Modane (France)–Bardonecchia (Italy)	8	868	13¼	1920
Arlberg	1884	St. Anton–Langen	6	639	3½	1925
Tauern	1909	Böckstein–Mallnitz	5	555	6	1933

with electrification the smoke menace has been removed but air is still blown into the Simplon to keep it cool.

American engineers have shown more skill in avoiding the construction of tunnels[1] than in their execution. The Hoosac tunnel, 9,270 yds. long, which connects New England with Albany was not completed until 1875 but it is the oldest of the long tunnels in the United States. In 1911 it was equipped for electric traction but is now worked by diesel-electric. The greatest American tunnels have been completed only in this generation: the Cascade tunnel, the longest in the western hemisphere, completed in 1929 and the Moffat tunnel under James Peak in Colorado which, opened in 1929, shortened the rail distance from Denver to Salt Lake City by 173 miles. When the C.P.R. was re-aligning the route over Rogers' Pass in the Selkirks the Connaught tunnel was bored and by lowering the rail summit 500 ft. a bank of 1 in 45 for 13½ miles was reduced to one of only a mile.

New Zealand with its mountainous terrain close to the coast has required special works; for example, the Raurimu spiral, the Rimutaka Incline and substantial tunnel construction. Between Wellington and Auckland is the Raurimu spiral to allow trains to ascend 430 ft. between places which are only 1¼ miles apart as the crow flies. The spiral has a gradient of 1 in 50 but, because of its length and consequent bottlenecking of traffic, had a crossing loop provided in 1953. The most powerful locomotives took 40 minutes to haul 330 tons up the 7 miles of spiral so this crossing has proved a great asset for operation. Ascent of the Rimutaka Mountains, with a rise of 871 ft. in 2½ miles, could not, without very heavy capital expenditure, be made with grades easier than 1 in 13 to 1 in 16 so the Fell system of working was adopted (p. 148). Even so to take a train up this incline a locomotive was allowed to haul only 65 tons at 6 m.p.h. This section, with braking troubles affecting downgrade operation also, became a bottleneck for traffic. A deviation line, with a tunnel nearly 5½ miles long to improve the gradient to 1 in 70 and shorten the route by 9 miles, is being constructed; it is estimated that with electric traction the new alignment will save an hour on the

[1] When the engineers were constructing the line between Bristol and Appalachia they were quick to utilise a natural tunnel, 788 ft. long, in a limestone spur of Powell Mountain.

journey between Masterton and Wellington. In the South Island there is only one rail route, opened in 1923, connecting the east and west coasts, and to complete this the Otira tunnel, 5⅛ miles long, had to be bored : the tunnel and its 1 in 33 western approach in Arthur's Pass are electrically worked.

Subterranean water

Water entering railway works can cause great trouble and is acute in the boring of tunnels for the quantity of water may be immense and tax the powers of the pumps. The classical British example of trouble from quicksands is the Kilsby tunnel where the rush of water drove out the tunnellers and bankrupted the contractor. Only by tremendous pumping and by lining with substantial brickwork was the water finally defeated. Water can also enter the workings along fissures. The working face on the Box tunnel between Bath and Chippenham was drowned out as a result of tapping fissures in the freestone while, because of water-carrying fissures, the Cheviet tunnel, near Wakefield, was lined with sheet lead until it was opened out into a cutting in 1924. The Apennine tunnel had to be waterproofed to prevent the track being constantly soaked. Hot springs were encountered during the boring of the Simplon tunnel while in the St. Gotthard bore the men were almost drowned when they tapped a great spring.

Wet ground

Saturated land offers treacherous foundations for the heavy earthworks of a railway and frequently such land has proved very difficult, if not impossible, to drain. George Stephenson met this obstacle when trying to cross Chat Moss between Liverpool and Manchester and he overcame it by spreading gravel on hurdles and "floating" the line across the bog. In the Netherlands, when it was desired to run fast trains after the war, it was realized that trouble would be caused by the weak layers of peat and clay in the section between Gouda and Oudewater—the Dutch Chat Moss—where the spongy subsoil normally had vertical oscillation with the passage of even a slow train and was also liable to sudden subsidence. In the post-war rehabilitation of the lines this danger section was conquered by laying broad sand berms and a raft of reinforced concrete under the track.

D

Wet ground in the muskeg area north of Lake Superior proved such a poor foundation that longer sleepers than usual had to be provided but even then the elasticity, before the track consolidated, led to rail spread and to train derailments. When the Central Alaskan line in from Seward was being constructed towards Fairbanks it was found that the broad U-shaped valleys, such as that of the Placer river, were so saturated by heavy floods from melting snows that the ground could not support embankments and trestles had to be built to carry the line across the wet area.

Flagler's extension of the line south of Miami was planned to run for 30 miles across the edge of the Everglades and to create an embankment in this terrain dredgers grabbed out debris from each side and piled it into a central embankment; the dredged cuts remained as drainage canals.

Valleys and areas of water

A valley athwart the line of a railway may be crossed by an embankment, by a viaduct or by a bridge. Embankments are frequently used because they avoid the need to create great spoil heaps for the disposal of the debris taken from cuttings and tunnels. Before an embankment is made the foundation width, which is wider than the track to allow for the angle of rest of the material to be dumped, is stripped of trees and soil and the culverts, to cope with the anticipated maximum run-off, are constructed before the material forming the embankment is tipped. Foundations have to be suitable and here again London Clay may be awkward: at Hanwell on the G.W.R. an embankment 54 ft. high pressed so heavily on its narrow base that the clay beneath was squeezed into a mound on one side of the line as the embankment itself sank. The material forming the embankment may cause trouble. Pyrites have set shales alight while clays, tipped for a year, have run everywhere except to build up the required embankment. Occasionally, the construction of the embankment has been used to reclaim land; on the Londonderry and Coleraine line 22,000 acres were so recovered from Lough Foyle.

Rivers are normally crossed by a bridge but in Dominica the Scottish-financed railway between La Vega and Sanchez uses a concreted ford for the track : when there is more than two feet of water over the track services are suspended. The number of bridges on a route may be very considerable : for example, in the 117 miles of the Chicago, Milwaukee and St. Paul R.R. along the Yellowstone valley the line crosses the meandering watercourse 115 times. It is said that in the U.S.A. there are over 190,000 railway bridges and, while relatively few are spectacular, all are essential to the iron road.

Bridges have been built of many materials. One of the earliest to be used was timber and this was adopted freely in Britain and the U.S.A. Some of the timber bridges had a long life. A wooden bridge across the Delaware, built in 1803 as a road bridge, was converted in 1848 for a railway and not replaced by an iron bridge until 1875. When seasoned timber was used the bridges were excellent but were liable to destruction by fire and decay. Frequently, sign of their pioneer period, the designs were bold : the original Portage Bridge, New York State, was 800 ft. long and 234 ft. high and contained $1\frac{1}{2}$ million B.M. of timber but, after it was burnt in 1875, was replaced by an iron trestle structure. Brunel was the British exponent of timber structures : along 60 miles of line in Cornwall he designed 34 viaduct bridges which had an aggregate length of four miles.

British and American practice differed over the way iron was used. Robert Stephenson, for example, favoured the massive type when he designed the Britannia Tubular Bridge over the Menai Straits, in which 4,680 tons of wrought-iron were consumed, and his bridge over the St. Lawrence. His American contemporary, Roebling, at this period was designing a much lighter Niagara Bridge, the first to span the gorge. Stephenson's designs still stand, although his St. Lawrence Bridge at Montreal has been greatly modified to take two tracks, but the lighter have had to be replaced. Much of this difference may be explained by the then relative poverty of the U.S.A. The American practice was to quote for a bridge as cost per foot-run. To satisfy the demand for low prices the weight of metal was kept to a minimum.

A particular form of bridge is where there is a movable span to allow navigation to continue although the bridge has a low clearance. These spans may either swing vertically or horizontally, be lifted up at both ends or slide telescopically. Moving spans are found in areas of low relief which are threaded by a navigable waterway : an example is the Keadby Bridge over the Trent.

Many of the world's notable bridges come from either the difficulty of obtaining foundations or of a base on which to erect falsework for masonry arches. When the Jubilee Bridge was being made across the Hooghly in Bengal one of the caissons for a pier was swept away by the bore. The Verrugas Bridge on the Oroya line, although only 718 ft. long and 246 ft. above the bed of the canyon, must rank as a noteworthy bridge because of heavy loss of life from fever among the labourers and from the difficulty of supplies. In a list of long bridges many of those of India appear but this is due to the nature of the valleys of the Indo-Gangetic plain for the flush of monsoon water can rise fast, spread widely and erode rapidly the banks despite the provision of long retaining walls (*bunds*) upstream of the bridges to restrict the channel. It is impossible even to refer to all the great bridges but the Table opposite summarizes the characteristics of a few in relation to the physical obstacles. The provision of these great and expensive structures is justified only by the shortening of the routes they affect.

The base of an embankment spreads over a considerable width and where land is valuable, as in towns, or else to avoid undue quantities of material having to be transported, if the rail-level is to be high above the surface, viaducts are frequently employed. In their construction, stone, brick, concrete, wood, iron and steel have all been used. Timber, light and quickly erected, has been used in Britain but now more permanent materials are used and in America, where tall-growing timber was available in the early days of railways, many tall timber trestle viaducts were built but some of these were later replaced by metal and others were converted into embankments.

There are many British examples of viaducts which are impressive from their size and also have an aesthetic value in the landscape : Dutton viaduct, over the River Weaver, with twenty red sandstone arches, each of 60-ft. span, regarded as George Stephenson's masterpiece, the Ouse viaduct towering 100 ft. above the river, the lofty Ribblehead viaduct of the Settle and Carlisle line and the graceful Leaderfoot viaduct over the Tweed where the Berwickshire line leaves the main line near Melrose.

SELECTED GREAT RAILWAY BRIDGES OF THE WORLD

Country	Name	Over	Length ft.	Rail Height above water ft.	Particular features
France	Fades	R. Sioule	—	434½	Highest bridge in world
Denmark	Storström	Masned Sd.	10,535	82	50 spans with 2 for navigation channels
Switzerland	Lorraine	R. Aar	3,609	—	Longest 4-track bridge in world : reinforced concrete main arch, 495-ft. span
Germany	Rendsborg	Kiel Canal	8,045	—	Cantilever, high-level mast clearance 181 ft.
Netherlands	Moerdijk	Hollandsch Diep	5,000	—	Embankment approaches to gain clearance
Gt. Britain	Britannia	Menai Strait	1,835	102	To span Menai Straits without delaying navigation
Gt. Britain	Forth	R. Forth estuary	7,268	156	Clearance required by Admiralty
Gt. Britain	Tay	R. Tay estuary	11,653	79½	Foundations in thick alluvium
Canada	Quebec	St. Lawrence	3,300	150	Ice in river
U.S.A.	Huey Long	Mississippi	22,997	142	—
Canada & U.S.A.	Niagara	Niagara gorge	780	226	—
Port. E. Africa	Lower Zambesi	R. Zambesi	11,650	—	River not navigable for ships
Rhodesias	Zambesi Falls	Zambesi gorge	500	420	Trestles rest on natural arch under which river flows
Burma	Gokteik	Chungzoune R.	2,260	325 ; 825	—
Australia	Hawkesbury	R. Hawkesbury	2,675	40	Foundations in estuarine mud
India	Curzon	Ganges	3,000	60	Protective bund to narrow stream 4,000 ft. long

These viaducts act as long bridges carrying the lines across wide valleys. Another excellent example of this is the Lethbridge viaduct of Alberta which, a mile long, carries the rail at a height of 314 ft. over the waters and valley of the Belly river. By providing this viaduct a stretch of line with sharp curves and steep gradients was eliminated.

Urban areas have also had extensive construction of viaducts. In New York, until the last service was stopped in 1955, was the elevated railway and in London is a series, particularly across the floodplain south of the Thames, of elevated lines built on brick arches. The Greenwich line, opened throughout in 1838, was laid on 878 arches for the $3\frac{3}{4}$ miles between London Bridge and Greenwich. The company, the first to operate a railway in the metropolis, intended to let the arches for dwellings and warehouses but they were far from ideal for these purposes. A boulevard was provided alongside the line and tolls were charged for promenading.

Viaducts occasionally cross tracts of water. One of the most impressive trestle viaducts ever conceived was that undertaken when Harriman secured control of the Union Pacific. The original alignment was north of the Great Salt Lake but this gave 373 miles of difficult haulage and, as traffic became heavier, it was essential to provide an easier route. The engineer planned the Lucin cut-off across the lake: this was a bold concept for the lake was regarded as unfathomable. For $27\frac{1}{2}$ miles, of which $15\frac{3}{4}$ were by embankment, the line was run across the lake with the track 19 ft. above the then water level.[1] Foundation difficulties occurred when the piles penetrated the salt crust and entered unstable sands. This cut-off shortened the route by $44\frac{3}{4}$ miles, avoided 1,515 ft. of climbing and speeded trains because many curves, equivalent to over eleven complete circles, were eliminated. The annual saving on operating was about one-twelfth of the capital cost but the original line was not abandoned until 1942 when the rails were lifted for military purposes. A fortunate feature of the site is that it has been found that the brine "pickles" the timber and so preserves it from decay.

[1] Variations in the level of the lake occur: the highest ever recorded was 4,216 ft. above sea-level in 1868 but this had shrunk to 4,199 ft. by 1902 and after a recovery to 4,208 ft. in 1924 was 4,198 ft. in 1944.

Another viaduct crossing water was the ferro-concrete structure across the sea from the mainland of Florida to Key West. Some thirty coral islands stretch over a great arc of 109 miles and the channels between were crossed by either embankments or arches with the rails at 31 ft. above low water. Drawbridges were provided over the navigable channels. Rail services were withdrawn after the 1935 hurricane had severely damaged the works but later the line was converted to a roadway.

An ingenious idea was tried by the engineer of the White Pass and Yukon line when he lowered the level of a lake by 14 ft., so as to be able to use the beach terrace exposed for his track, but the bar he cut through to the required depth was a morainic dump and the flush of escaping water so scoured the outlet channel that the lake was lowered by 70 ft. and he was then able at the cost of two large bridges, to cut directly across the lake bed.

Bridging has also on occasion been done along the axis of valleys. In Germany a unique development was to span above the River Wüpper with girders and to hang the train from a mono-rail. With an orthodox railway too bridges have been made along the axis of a river. When Colorado was being threaded by railways to allow its mineral wealth to be exploited the Arkansas river, except for the 9½ miles of the Royal Gorge, was the obvious alignment for one route. It was possible to use a ledge for part of the way along this gorge but there was a section, only 30 ft. wide, where the river cataracted between canyon walls nearly 3,000 ft. high. Tunnelling was too slow and too expensive so cross-girders were placed between the walls of the canyon and the track hung from these.

Waterways have also been crossed by tunnels where bridging is difficult, for example, the Severn and the Hudson. The Severn estuary is crossed at the Shoots where the river is 50 ft. deep. The approaches are given a gradient of 1 in 100 and the tunnel section is over 23,000 ft. long. Construction proved so formidable, with an irruption of fresh water from the Great Spring in 1879 and of salt water two years later, that it looked as if the scheme might have to be abandoned. Clay was dumped on the river-bed to choke the hole by which the sea-water entered and then, by heavy pumping, the works were cleared of water. In 1885 the last of 77 million bricks used in the lining was laid but soon the pressure of the Great Spring partially crushed the brickwork and there is still constant pumping to keep the tunnel free of water; 20 million gallons a day are removed. The opening of this tunnel reduced the journey distance between Swindon and Newport by 25 miles as compared with that *via* Gloucester, but the company was allowed to charge as for 12 miles instead of the actual 4½.

In Asia an undersea tunnel is that joining Honshu to Kyushu which, opened in 1942, reduced the journey time across the Straits of Shimonoseki from one hour by sea to ten minutes.

North America has some important rivers crossed by tunnels, for example, the St. Clair. This river links Lakes Huron and Ontario, and, nearly half a mile wide, flows swiftly in summer after the winter freeze. Ferries were used for transporting railway wagons but there was constant interference with the cross-river service because of the substantial traffic passing between the lakes. A bridge was impossible: low banks prevented adequate headroom for steamships and the frequency of water traffic meant a moving span would lead to delays on both media. Instead of trying to bridge this obstacle the engineers decided to tunnel. This tunnel, through morainic clay, was lined with iron segments. It was opened in 1890 and since then has carried an immense traffic between Canada and the United States. It only has single track and, with its steep approach gradients, proved a difficult bottleneck which was not made any easier to work by the locomotives belching out smoke and steam as they laboured up the exit slope. In 1908 it became one of the first main lines to be electrified despite the handicap of a maximum clearance of only 15 ft. 6 in. under the overhead conductor: this restricts the rolling stock which can pass.

The physical form and nature of the land surface greatly affect the work of the railway engineer but even with exactly comparable physical conditions the solution is unlikely to be the same because so much depends upon the anticipated traffic flow and also on the availability of capital at the time of planning the route. The landforms are not the only physical factors which influence railways and the next chapter is concerned with atmospheric effects.

CHAPTER IV

FOG AND FLOOD

CLIMATE and weather can affect the construction and operation of railways: a wet season, a torrential downpour, snow, ice or gales can alter the conditions and can damage the works and lead to disaster.

Desert areas

Hot deserts, in particular, offer problems for both the engineer and the management. Construction of the Otavi line, inland from Swakopmund, was greatly hindered by the aridity of South West Africa. Despite many attempts to find water by boring nothing but brackish water was discovered in the first 85 miles and every drop needed during the construction had to be carried in from the port. When the Lucin cut-off was being constructed, it required 103 miles of new line across an arid area of Utah; 1,700 tons of water had to be carried in daily. Although the introduction of diesel operation eliminates the need of water haulage for steam-raising it is still required for railway settlements *en route*.

Wet seasons and cloudbursts

Tropical monsoon lands provide problems for the management. During the monsoon period the cab of the locomotive is enclosed to protect the footplate crew from the rain while during this season there is the constant risk of damage to the track by washouts. In the black-earth lands of the Deccan the rains turn the soil into a glutinaceous mass and repair work is made most difficult at the time it is most needed. The 2-ft. gauge Darjeeling line penetrates into the foothills of the Himalayas where the average annual rainfall is about 120 in.: bad as this is for track maintenance the occasional abnormal falls, for example 14 in. in six hours, are more devastating. Another district where the wet season has a heavy precipitation is eastern Brazil. Here the

Leopoldina line runs in a region with 100 in. of rain in the wet period: bridges are subjected to the pressure of rivers in spate, landslides occur frequently and the line is flooded and may be ripped away by the force of the torrent. An amusing effect of the wet season was experienced when the Nyasaland line was being constructed: at the onset of the wet season the whole of the local labour force decamped in order to cultivate their crops.

The regular wet season rains may be countered in the design but it is less simple to estimate for the exceptional rainfall in a semi-arid regime. In such a region the total average precipitation may not be great but it can be so concentrated into a few hours that works can be swept away in a sudden downpour which is unable to penetrate quickly into parched land, and runs off as a sheet of water. Material for embankments is frequently obtained from "borrow-pits" alongside the track and, to prevent gully-erosion forming during a torrential downpour, these are made discontinuous in semi-arid regions. Heavy floods are rare, but can be catastrophic; in Australia, as a safety measure, bridges are provided with wide spans. The Katherine river (Northern Territory) has been known to rise by more than 70 ft. In addition to rising so high that the girders of a bridge can be swept away floods can also scour out the foundations; this happened to the piers of the Albert Bridge, Brisbane, in 1893.

Cloudbursts have caused a number of railway accidents. In 1914 a sudden thunderstorm in the hills near Carr Bridge on the Highland Railway caused the Baddengorm Burn to rise rapidly and to carry down tree-trunks which choked the arch of the bridge under the railway. This collapsed under the weight of a passing train and five passengers were drowned: this was the worst accident on a railway in the Highlands of Scotland. Curiously a similar mishap occurred at the same point in 1923 but fortunately, although more of the line was swept away, no train was involved. In 1923 at Woodford in the Tehachapi mountains of California water, as a result of a cloudburst, rushed down a canyon as a wall 40 ft. high and swept away fifteen bridges and a locomotive.

One of the most troublesome bridges ever built was the Verrugas Bridge (*see* p. 52). After the bridge had been completed, despite the ravages of *Verrugas fever*, it was completely wrecked by a cloudburst which started a landslide: the new bridge was built as a cantilever to avoid a recurrence of the disaster destroying the central pier. Equivalent in its action to a cloudburst was the rupture in 1934 of a glacier which dammed a lake in the Andes. The water swept down to the Mendoza valley and ripped away miles of track and the Transandine line was abandoned until the flow of traffic, to meet wartime needs, led to its reconstruction in 1944.

Snow

Snow has long been feared in railway operating although not so timorously as when at the opening day in 1839 of the Frankfort and Lexington Railway, in Kentucky, the driver deserted the train and put the locomotive in a shed because of a snow flurry. Snow can hinder operations in a number of ways—by choking the draught of the fire, by sweeping in an avalanche over the line, by obscuring the signals or by clogging moving parts and causing them to fail to respond to the signal levers. Conditions are trying for the operating staff and in Scandinavia locomotive cabs have shutters to protect the footplate crew.

Even with the great heat of a locomotive firebox the airgaps at the edge of the ash-pan have been known to get covered with a hard layer of snow and, by starving the fire of oxygen, lead to stoppage because the driver was unable to get sufficient head of steam.

In a number of years the railway system of Britain has had sections completely paralysed by the snow cover. On the 3rd of March, 1881, a blizzard closed the Settle and Carlisle line and the tracks were covered in snow which was in places 40 ft. deep. This same storm drifted over 111 miles of routes on the G.W.R. in Berkshire and Wiltshire. Two years before this all trains on the Highland line south of Inverness were stopped by the snowdrifts and it was announced in the Highland capital, "The whereabouts of the 3.10 p.m. Sunday Mail was to the officials on Monday night an absolute mystery." Snow accumulation which can close a line is common at high altitudes—at the Bernice Hospice station in Switzerland as much as 20 ft. piles upon the track—and at high latitudes—on the White Pass and Yukon line the snow drifts are as much as 35 ft. thick.

American railways have been repeatedly cloyed-up by impalpable snow. The greatest blizzard ever recorded in the Great Plains hit western Nebraska and eastern Wyoming January 2nd–5th, 1949, and every line in the main storm area was closed. On the Union Pacific system about forty trains were stopped, food had to be flown to marooned passengers while aeroplanes were chartered to fly charcoal to Cheyenne to heat the cars of fruit expresses. The cost to the Union Pacific and the Burlington systems alone was, for each, over a million dollars.

Drifting of snow is a major problem particularly in cuttings where the slight hollows have lee areas which slacken the speed of air currents and cause the drifting snow to settle. On some lines snow is kept from drifting by providing screens parallel to, but away from, the line in order to create a quiet pocket away from the track in which the snow will settle. Snow-blowers can also be used: these solid screens concentrate the air blowing across the track so as to reduce any tendency to slacken speed. No matter what devices are used snow can settle on a line. Thin covers can be pushed aside by scoops in front of the locomotive wheels and larger ploughs, pushed by one or more locomotives, can remove such thick drifts as normally occur in Britain. With more substantial accumulations of snow the rotary plough, with knives driven by a steam engine, can fling the snow clear of the track. These knife-blades have to be rotated rapidly and if they hit a balk of timber or a boulder embedded in the snow the rotary plough is ruined in a second. In post-war years melting of the snow has been tried but usually it is difficult to provide a run-off for the melt-water. Snow melters have been tried in Canadian marshalling yards: the snow is lifted into tank wagons by a conveyor belt, melted in these and discharged outside the yard.

Snow avalanches down mountainsides and, to avoid the destruction of the lines, snowsheds are constructed to carry the avalanches clear of the track: on one route over the North American Sierra Nevada there are over 60 miles of these snowsheds. The volume of snow in an avalanche may be tremendous and damage is also done by the air-blast created by the snow rushing down the mountainside. Trains can be hurled off the track and steel rails snapped like matchsticks. On the C.P.R. route across Rogers' Pass, before the Connaught tunnel was opened in 1915, there was a section with 4½ miles of snowsheds. Unbroken sheds on a steep bank result, with steam operation, in the driver's view of the track ahead being obscured by smoke and the snowsheds on this section were limited to 3,000 ft. in length with an adequate gap between. To prevent avalanches destroying the open sections great V-fences, with the apex pointing uphill, were placed on the mountainside so that the avalanches would be split and turned to pass over the snowsheds. All this disability and the expense of rotary snowploughs for the open sections was avoided when the tunnel was provided.

In Switzerland across the Steffenbach Gorge on the Furka-Oberalp line was a bridge which was destroyed by an avalanche. The line was only open for traffic from June to September so, instead of rebuilding it as before, a movable bridge was constructed and it is dismantled and lifted out of harm's way before each winter. Since the Arlberg line was first opened in 1884 about £25 million has been spent on protective works because of the avalanche danger. Most attention has been paid to the 16 miles between Braz and Langen because of the frequency of avalanches in this section. In one period of 24 hours in 1954 104 avalanches struck across the Arlberg route. Forest belts have been planted and protective walls made high on the mountainsides above the railway in an endeavour to prevent the avalanches developing. Many sections of the Central Alaskan line have been wrecked by the numerous avalanches of early summer. When the surveyors were planning a route through the Feather River canyon, in the Cascades, they ignored the easier side, which was followed by the Indian trail, because it was on the shady side and had much thicker falls of snow and a greater avalanche risk.

During a snowstorm in 1876 there was a serious accident in Britain from snow clogging under a signal arm and preventing it from being raised to the danger position. Now many signals work to the upper quadrant in such a manner that snow cannot clog.

Besides the snow itself the natural melt may cause trouble. Along the route of the Transandine line melting snow-waters cause rock disintegrated by frost to move as mud-flows and these have in places shifted the track downhill. Melting of the snow causes rivers to flood and along the Mendoza valley the scree slopes, alluvial terraces and conglomerates can be rapidly eroded with destruction of the track laid on such a material.

Ice

Only rarely has the presence of ice been an advantage to railway working: two of the best-known instances were the laying of temporary lines across the St. Lawrence and Lake Baikal. The line across the St. Lawrence was first laid in 1880 and tried for three winters, but the public lacked confidence in the method because a locomotive depressed the track until it slipped and the engine slid through the ice into 30 ft. of water. Crossing of Lake Baikal by an ice-bridge was much more successful and was used until the opening of the avoiding line round the south of the lake. Two ice-breakers, constructed at Newcastle and reassembled on the shores of Lake Baikal, for a time maintained the connection at the periods of thaw and freeze.

Ice-floes on rivers can cause damage to railway bridges. The Solway Viaduct between England and Scotland was severely damaged by ice floes in 1881–2. When Robert Stephenson was engineer for the Victoria Bridge across the St. Lawrence River at Montreal he specially designed the piers to cut the ice-floes and at the same time prevent them jamming and rising to the height of the track.

Wet cement disintegrates if frozen while it is setting and during the construction of the Siberian Railway, to allow the construction work to proceed, heated shelters were placed over masonry structures during the winter. Freezing also heaves the surface and during the building of the Hudson Bay line to Churchill, 1926–31, winter frosts as severe as −60°F. acted on the muskeg and damaged the works so much that they had to be relaid.

Ice forming on wires, rails and gear is a hindrance if not an actual danger. In frosty weather rain falling on the telegraph and telephone wires, on which so much operational efficiency depends, can freeze round the wires, and the added weight and larger surface make them vulnerable to destruction with strong gusts of wind. In 1872 many of the wires of Britain were brought down and traffic conditions rendered chaotic. A glaze frost on the third-rail insulates it so effectively that the shoe cannot pick up the current: this occurred in the winter 1939–40 in London, and so now the electrified suburban lines of London have steam locomotives running over the routes with special brushes to take the ice-skin off the top of the third-rail. Points are also vulnerable to being frozen and at important freight-yards in Canada propane gas heaters have been placed under the points in order to melt the ice and to maintain free movement. Water-troughs for locomotive purposes have never been widely used in the U.S.A. but where they have been adopted arrangements have often been made to heat them because of the severe frosts experienced. Accidents have occurred from condensed water freezing in the pipes which run the length of a train to operate the automatic brakes; the ice forms a plug and the device is rendered useless and becomes a danger because the train crew may not realize they have lost braking power.

High temperatures

High temperatures produce difficulties for railways. During the boring of the Alpine tunnels the heat at the working face could be insufferable but the use of compressed air for drilling did improve conditions for it not only brought a stream of fresh air but also it cooled as it expanded after working the drills. Although forced ventilation has been used in the London Tubes since 1903, the temperature is slowly rising from an accumulation of heat in the London Clay; the "hot-spot" is Kensington to Balham, 77–78°F. On the surface too high temperatures can give very trying physical conditions. During the construction of a section of the Trans-Saharan Railway during the war the slave-labour, without adequate clothes or shelter, suffered from the 70°F. diurnal range.

In operation one of the most serious difficulties experienced with a rise of temperature is expansion of steel rails. The coefficient of expansion per °F. is 0·00002 and with each 60 ft. of rail this means that with a rise of temperature of 100°F. (56°C.) there is an increase of length of $\frac{1}{8}$ in.: to counteract this gaps are left between the rail lengths but it may not always be adequate, particularly when there has been rail-creep tending to close the gap. Rail movement from expansion leads to constant watching of the track for keys, which hold other than flat-bottomed track in chairs, tend to be loosened, and yet there must be some play, particularly with the fishplates which join the rails, or the rails can buckle with expansion. In recent years rails have been welded together in long lengths (*see* p. 15) and despite this it has been found that, if the rail is held firmly, with frequent anchors to the ground, there is no expansion trouble.

In hot climates train crew and passengers suffer considerable discomfort. In India wooden louvres are fitted to allow air to enter but, like venetian blinds, keep out the direct rays of the sun while in the modern first-class carriages of the Gold Coast Railway darkened glass is fitted. Cooling of coaches by placing large blocks of ice in the compartments was used on Indian railways before air-conditioning by modern methods had been invented. The Baltimore and Ohio R.R. had experimented with cooling by ice of passenger coaches in 1884 and in 1930 put into service the first mechanically air-conditioned coach.

Fog

Fog is one of the most dreaded weather conditions for railway operation. In estuarine districts, with a natural tendency to mist and its potency made worse by smoke from coal-fires, fog is a major menace. Unfortunately such districts, as the London region, are also those with a high frequency of traffic where train delays can have wide repercussions.

In the 'eighties London and the Midlands were plagued by several severe fogs, which lingered for days. In a dense fog not only are trains delayed but the costs of operation, at a time when fog makes the traffic dwindle, become greater: there is the cost of fog-signals, of extra lighting and of overtime for the men who have to be taken off their proper duties to act as special signalmen because the usual visual signals are rendered useless. The modern electric light signal can penetrate fog more effectively but its message may be missed and the only real solution is the provision of track apparatus which will repeat in the cab of the locomotive the information conveyed by the lineside signal. While the pea-soup fog, or to give its modern name "smog", is becoming more rare there is still the menace of the clean fog which cannot be changed as it is a natural phenomenon.

Winds and gales

The movement of air need not be very rapid to affect railways and it need not be an adverse effect. The tunnel beneath Beckwourth Pass, which carries the Western Pacific line across the Cascades, funnels the chinook winds which melt the snow on the adjacent open sections and obviates the need to provide snow-sheds.

Unfortunately wind is more often a cause of trouble, particularly if "teeth" can be given to its force by a load such as sand. On the former line to Burghead in Scotland drifting sand choked the track and "sand-blowers", sheets of iron placed obliquely to the track to prevent eddy currents forming, were provided. Sections of the Siberian Railway are troubled by sand-storms which sweep in from the desert while in the Mallee District (Victoria, Australia) over 13 miles of wind-chute fencing have been erected to prevent sand being deposited on the track. The fencing consists of a sloping fence, up to 30 ft. high and with a gap of 3 ft. at the bottom, facing into the prevailing wind. The lee slopes of cuttings are flattened. The slope of the fence accelerates the passage of the air across the track and so sand is not so liable to be deposited. Sand may also be a nuisance to the engine and on the Sfax–Gafsa line in Tunisia the discharge from the diesel locomotives is from the roof away from the sand on which the track is laid.

Strong winds can affect the power of a locomotive and, as with frosty weather, the load may have to be reduced or time be lost on the journey. More disastrous than this is the effect of gales on structures: the Tay Bridge collapse of 1879 and the destruction of the Key West line in 1935 are examples of such troubles. The Tay Bridge collapsed while a train was crossing a few months after its completion. The disaster was brought about by faulty workmanship and design; the force of the wind in this estuary had not been appreciated by the designer. Before such a structure were erected now there would be wind-tunnel experiments to assess the forces likely to play on the super-structure. On a narrow-gauge Irish line in West Kerry, after a gale had blown a train off the track at Quilty in the winter of 1898–9, an anemometer was installed and the passage of a train is forbidden when the wind speed exceeds 80 m.p.h. In January,

1925, a train was blown off the Owencarrow Viaduct, in north Donegal, where the westerly winds are funnelled, and following this accident an anemometer was installed and trains stopped during gales. After a gale in 1880 which blew a train off the track, with a loss of life, a "Siberia" windshield was installed along some viaducts on the Rimutaka Incline to protect the trains.

Winds acting on water can damage railways. The G.W.R. along the western side of the Exe estuary is close to the shore, and, with a long fetch of water, is liable to damage and has needed repeated repair. Storms have damaged the works of the Lucin cut-off because the dense water of Great Salt Lake can lift large blocks of stone and after storm damage in 1923 and 1924 the embankment was strengthened and raised to 15 ft. above the then lake level (*see* p. 54). The Chiromo Bridge, which carries the line from Blantyre to Port Herald in Nyasaland, across the Shire river, was swept away in 1948 by the weight of great masses of sudd which had been previously loosened by high winds.

CHAPTER V

MOTIVE POWER

SINCE the classic locomotive trials at Rainhill for the Liverpool and Manchester Railway in 1829, the consensus of opinion has been to have the engine moving with the load and not to rely on cable or other devices to haul trains along. For four generations the steam locomotive maintained its supremacy because of its low capital cost, simplicity of working and maintenance and capacity for hard work, but there have been variations in the design to suit local conditions. The principal features in which the geographical conditions have influenced design and operation have been in fuel, water supply, capacity for handling on gradients and sharp curves. Rivals to the reciprocating steam locomotive have been tried since the days of the trials when the *Rocket* alone fulfilled the conditions, for one of the entries was driven by a horse walking along a track set on a geared truck. Engineers and inventors have been prolific in their ideas—for example, the "atmospheric" tube, the moving rope, the electric battery; most have been unpracticable but they have included the successful alternatives of electric propulsion and diesel engines. Experiments which seemed to offer distinct prospects, but have not hitherto been adopted extensively, include the turbine locomotive and the Drumm battery locomotive. In this chapter consideration will be given first to the factors affecting steam locomotives and then to electric and diesel engines. Both diesel and electric locomotives have an advantage over the steam in that less time is required for locomotive duties, turning is unnecessary and so terminal capacity is appreciably increased, acceleration is more rapid, thus increasing line capacity, fuel is not consumed except when at work and stations can be kept cleaner. British experience suggests that electric power is more reliable than diesel but our experience is, as yet, too limited to judge. Designs of steam locomotives, with rivalry, have been improved and power has been greatly increased. Giants, such as the Chesapeake and

Ohio Railway 2-6-6-6 *Mallets* with a tractive effort of 110,200 lb. were evolved to handle coal trains. The steam locomotive provides horse-power at a lower initial cost than any other source but this advantage has dwindled somewhat since the war.

COST OF LOCOMOTIVES, IN U.S. DOLLARS

Large steam locomotive			*Diesel-electric*
1939	...	150,000	550,000
1949	...	350,000	600,000

STEAM LOCOMOTIVES

Fuel Supply

Coal. The traditional fuel is coal but the generic term includes a wide range of qualities. Locomotive coal of a good quality is in large lumps because dusty coal is blown out unburnt by the force of the great draught in a firebox. Finely pulverized coal can be used but it must be mechanically fed into the firebox. Coal-dust, blown into a suitably constructed combustion chamber, burns rapidly with an intense heat for each carbon particle is exposed to oxygen and is consumed almost immediately.

Good locomotive coals, such as the Blidworth, have calorific values of about 13,000 British Thermal Units (B.Th.U.) per lb. Before the 1939–45 war the supply of good quality steam coal in large lumps was not the general problem that it is now. Poor quality coals demand large fireboxes: such abnormally large fireboxes are found in India to cope with the Indian coal which is of low calorific value. Combustion has to be rapid in order to cope with the steam consumption and to superheat to 700°F. Even with the best designs of fireboxes and boilers about one quarter of the calorific value of the fuel is lost in this conversion.

In Australia, coal from Newcastle, New South Wales, with a calorific value of 12,600 B.Th.U., is used but cost of haulage and shortage of supplies are problems. In Western Australia Collie coal is used, because of the cost of importing better coals, although it has a 20 per cent moisture content, very readily disintegrates and has a calorific value of only 9,500 B.Th.U. With the shortage of Newcastle coal the Victorian State Railways since 1947 have been using some locomotives fitted with the Henschel apparatus to burn pulverized brown coal produced in the Yalbourn area: this has required the provision of special tank-wagons to carry the pulverized fuel.

Coal consumption varies with the load and with the speed and in recent years, as a result of proper testing stations such as that at Rugby, more knowledge has been obtained of the factors affecting consumption. For example, using Blidworth coal with a calorific value of 12,600 B.Th.U. the new British Railway Class 5 4-6-0 mixed traffic locomotive uses coal at the following rates per ton-mile on a level track with a freight train at 40 m.p.h.[1]

Train load, tons	Coal consumption, lb.
250	0·086
350	0·071
500	0·066
800	0·059

These figures show that the heavier trains are slightly more economical on coal consumption.

Oil fuel. Apart from its use in oil-driven engines fuel-oil has also been used in place of coal for steam-raising. In Britain the first experiments were made about 1890 when on the G.E.R. the *Petrolea* ran using an oily waste from the Company's gasworks. The experiments were successful, and consumed what was then a troublesome by-product but the rising cost of oil led to a reversion to coal. Since then whenever coal has been scarce, as during a coal strike or with the aftermath of war, locomotives have been fitted with oil-tanks and "atomizers" to burn the fuel but have been reconverted as coal supplies became easier. Oil is regularly used as a fuel in oil-producing regions such as southern Russia and Rumania but it is not such a satisfactory way of obtaining the power from the oil because the oil-engine has a higher thermal efficiency. One advantage, compared with coal, is that one ton of oil has a heating value of about double that of a ton of coal and other advantages are that it eases the footplate work and

[1] B.T.C. *Locomotive Testing Bull. No. 6.*

eliminates the risk of burning lineside crops and forests. It was the fire hazard that led to the Victorian State Railways adapting a number of locomotives to oil-burning. It is doubtful if with coal firemen could cope with the immense labour of stoking the fires of the giant locomotives used on the Peruvian Central line: these engines consume 24 tons of steam an hour in the arduous ascent. The fuel used may vary with circumstances: until 1900 the Kenya-Uganda line imported Welsh coal but when the railway reached the forested highlands there was a change to wood: in 1926 coal was again imported for the first *Beyer-Garratts*, but this time it was South African coal, and since 1948 these locomotives have, with increasing cost of coal, been converted to oil-burning.

Petrol. This fuel has been principally used for railcars and it has proved convenient for these small units because an ordinary clutch and gear can be used as with a road vehicle. Some of these railcars are fitted with rubber-tyred wheels and travel quietly, others have two sets of wheels so they can be run on either road or rail.

Wood. This fuel is bulky and of low calorific value, about one-third of that of coal, and also requires for combustion more air than coal. When wood is used the effect is seen in the locomotive design and in the services. On the Bolivian locomotives which use wood fuel larger airgaps are allowed between the firebars because, at 12,000 ft. above sea-level, the rarefied atmosphere slows up combustion.[1] Fireboxes have to be large when wood is used.

Because wood is so bulky the calorific value of the load of fuel which can be carried is limited and very long-distance runs cannot be made as there is need to refuel. In Victoria (Australia) it was found that on a run of 100 miles a freight train had to refuel at three points *en route*. Again the weight which may be hauled is limited and when railways have had to turn to wood, in times of emergency, loads have had to be drastically reduced.

[1] This rarefied air causes passengers to suffer from mountain sickness (*soroche*) and on some of the Andean trains cylinders of oxygen are carried to ease the malaise. Other travellers break the journey for a night at about 8,000 ft. in order to get acclimatized.

If the locomotive is designed for wood burning it may still be powerful: in Siam loads of over 500 tons are hauled with wood as a fuel.

With wood fuel regularly used locomotives are fitted with spark arrestors and this is a conspicuous piece of equipment on some Finnish and Russian locomotives. During the post-war coal shortage in Victoria (Australia) wood fuel was used from May 24th until October 19th, 1946, but it was discontinued during the warmer weather because of the fire-hazard.

Miscellaneous fuels. Various other materials have also been used as fuels: in Sweden pulverized peat, in Siam rice husks, in Brazil coffee-beans, in Argentina maize. Many of these fuels are only used either in times of coal shortage or because of low prices on the world markets for the material being burnt. They are all bulky in relation to their calorific value.

Water supply

Supply of water for steam-raising is a major problem in many semi-arid areas—not merely in the quantity but also in the quality of the water. On the projected Trans-Saharan route there is no surface supply between Colomb–Béchar and Tabankort and so diesel working is the only practical solution when, and if, the line is completed.

In Nigeria, between Kano and N'Guru, 137 miles, water is only obtainable at one place so all steam trains haul supplementary water-tanks as also did steam trains which formerly crossed the Nullabor Plain of Australia. In order to operate trains on the Johannesburg–Mafeking line the Beyer-Garratt locomotives are provided with additional water-tanks so they carry 8,500 gallons to provide, despite limited watering-points, for their great steam consumption. The locomotives which handle the coal traffic of the Donbas region have a tank capacity of 11,500 gallons. The increase of post-war traffic in East Africa has intensified the water-supply problems particularly on the Mombasa–Nairobi section where the River Tsavo is the only permanent surface water. Unfortunately the supply from bore-holes is declining and pipelines will have to be provided possibly from as far as springs on the flanks of Kilimanjaro.

The quality of the water affects locomotive performance and maintenance for scale from hard water both insulates and is difficult to remove. Softeners may be used either at the supply point or on the locomotive and in South Africa four-fifths of all locomotives now use chemically softened water. In the semi-arid Tucuman region of Argentina the water is so corrosive that to avoid taking local supplies, condensers have been fitted to some locomotives since 1931 and by this device engines can run nearly 500 miles before taking on more water. Condensers are also used where, as on the Turksib line of Turkestan, water of any kind is in short supply. The main water-supply problem in South Africa is the busy main line from De Aar to Touws river but other difficult sections are De Aar–Windhoek and the Mafeking line and on this last section condensing locomotives, which can run without watering 700 miles instead of 50, have been used since 1949. Electrification or diesel working would have avoided the deadweight haulage of the condenser, a tender fitted with the apparatus and carrying 19 tons of coal weighs 109½ tons, but coal is relatively cheap and its continued use therefore attractive. The shortage of water may ultimately reduce the number of trains. Various experimental turbine-locomotives have been built and most use a condenser which adds to the efficiency of the turbine and reduces the demands on a water-supply. With the condensing plant, and therefore without the exhaust-induced draught, a fan must be provided to get sufficient oxygen into the firebox.

When the railway was extended inland in Western Australia, in order to develop the valuable gold deposits, water-supply became a major problem because the local supplies, even when rainfall was caught in reservoirs, were heavily charged with chemicals. At Coolgardie (1899) and at Geraldton (1904), therefore, distilling apparatus was installed to provide pure water which would not harm the boilers. Although 60,000 gallons a day were obtainable from the plant at Coolgardie the supply was inadequate and now water is piped alongside the line for 350 miles from the Darling Range, fifteen miles east of Perth. For the cooling of the diesel engines used in Western Australia and elsewhere chromated water is used but the quantities required are negligible.

A device, now 100 years old, is the water trough which allows locomotives to pick up water while travelling at speed. This is valuable because it removes an incubus on long non-stop journeys and also it gives some latitude in the choice of watering points and helps to avoid drawing on supplies of unsuitable water. A major advantage is that it reduces the deadweight to be hauled in that a smaller tender can be used because the watering troughs can be close enough to allow frequent refilling of the tender. Evolved by an engineer of the L.N.W.R. the device was slow in finding general favour other than on the home line, possibly because of the royalties charged on its use, and was only really utilized, outside England, on the systems of the New York Central R.R. and Pennsylvania R.R. in the United States. To be effective a flat, well-drained track is required and there must be little risk of freezing unless a heating system is also installed. In areas, such as Scotland, where even long-distance trains stop frequently at stations with an abundant supply of soft water, there is not the same incentive to provide troughs.

Gradients

When gradients are associated with sharp curves they greatly affect the performance of locomotives and may require special designs. One modification for steep gradients is to use small diameter driving wheels, for example, 3 ft. 9 in. on the Beyer-Garratt locomotives used on the steep ascent from Callao to the Peruvian copper mines. Unless small diameter wheels are used the engine can do little more than pull its own weight but small wheels require a large boiler capacity, for each movement of the piston only moves the engine a small distance along the rails, and to cover a mile the cylinders have to be filled more often than with large diameter wheels.

Where gradients vary greatly along a route and include sections which tax the power of the locomotives the alternatives are to reduce the load throughout the journey to that which can be handled by the locomotive on the steepest section, or to add banking engines for the difficult sections or to split the train for these banks. The first demands the provision of engine-power redundant for most of the journey, and crews, for the relief trains, over the whole route while the last method leads to considerable marshalling delays but is used on difficult grades such as the Rimutaka north of Wellington. The second method is most widely adopted and examples can be drawn from England (the Lickey Incline) and Canada (the Kicking Horse Pass where powerful 2–10–4 banking locomotives were used until dieselization).

Descent of steep gradients taxes the braking power of the train and can lead to overheating of the wheels. Devices to aid braking include steam brakes and counter-pressure brakes. On the Kalka–Simla line, and on some of the long descending gradients of the western cordillera of North America, jets of water are sprayed on the tyres during descents to prevent them overheating with the friction from the brake-blocks. On British Railways, because few goods vehicles are fitted with automatic brakes which can be worked from the locomotive, the regulations for each steep down-gradient instruct the guards to "drop" a given number of brakes to slacken the momentum and so allow the footplate crew to keep the train under control : time is consumed at the top and bottom of the bank dropping and lifting these wagon brakes.

Curves

A particular problem of locomotive design is to get the power without placing excessive weight on the track or making the engine so long that it cannot round bends. The simple bogie or radial truck allows curves to be tackled at speed as the locomotive is, by its use, gently eased round the curve and can adapt itself to inequalities of the track. When Robert Stephenson went in 1853 to Canada to advise on the construction of the bridge across the St. Lawrence he travelled from Portland (Maine) to Montreal and an account of the journey, written by his travelling companion, is preserved.

"The railway through the White Mountain district had only been opened a few days, and we were told that many of the embankments had sunk 5 or 6 feet . . . we found the embankments looking more like hollows between the crests of waves in the Atlantic. . . . Mr. Stephenson and myself [S. Bidder] stood on the platform of the cars, and had to hold on to the rails by both hands, as hard as possible, to prevent ourselves from being thrown off, for over this road we went, and round curves not more than 200 yards radius, at a speed of 15 to 20 miles an hour. . . . [Mr. Stephenson] said it was the most dangerous ride he had ever had in his life. . . . An engine built on the principle of those now used in England would not have kept on the rails a hundred yards and yet this Bogie engine took us a distance of 58 miles, over such a road as I have described, in perfect safety."[1]

Rough track, sharp curves and steep gradients are the bane of fast running.

One design which can work on sharp curves is the *Fairlie* which consists of two boilers, with a common firebox, which provide steam for two sets of cylinders. As the boilers are set on bogies the locomotive can round sharp curves for there is no long fixed wheel-base. The Fairlie type was adopted on narrow-gauge lines, such as the Welsh Highland Railway (Portmadoc to Blaenau Ffestiniog), while for the standard gauge lines the *Mallet* type has been more popular. This consists of an ordinary boiler carried on two swivelling trucks. The most common form of articulated locomotive is the *Beyer-Garratt* which consists of a very large boiler supported on two chassis trucks each with a complete driving gear. One chassis also carries the coal supply and the other the water whereas the Mallet type has a tender to carry fuel and water supplies. These articulated types are the equivalent of two locomotives and have the advantages of requiring only one crew, of spreading the weight along the track, as well as of being able to round curves. The *Kitson-Meyer* articulated locomotive as used in Colombia, can round a curve the radius of which is only four times its own length. The Garratts are used in Britain for heavy coal trains and also in India, South Africa and the Andean lines. Beyer-Garratts were introduced on to the Rhodesian Railways in 1926 and by 1954 they provided three-fifths of the tractive effort of the system: the latest giants have a tractive effort of 69,330 lb.: yet an axle-load of only 17 tons.

Ephraim Shay invented in 1880 the popular *Shay* type of an

[1] J. C. Jeaffreson, *Life of Robert Stephenson*. London, 1864, ii, pp. 180–1.

articulated, geared locomotive, with vertical cylinders and off-centre boiler, to get lumber out of Michigan woods : in 1945 the Western Maryland Railway purchased a Shay locomotive to handle coal traffic on the tortuous Vindex colliery branch but within eight years it was presented to a museum because of the dieselization programme.

With sharp curves the wheel flanges get ground away and on such curves on the Central Peruvian line oil is used to lubricate the side of the rail. The oil must be kept away from the top of the rail otherwise the driving wheels would slip ; the train would stall on ascents and get out of control on descents.

ELECTRIC HAULAGE

Because electric motors were invented later than the recipro-cating steam locomotive the use of electricity has had to be adopted in the face of a proven agent, the powers of which were well known. In 1920 it appeared as if the steam locomotive was doomed by the superior efficiency of electricity, witness a con-vincing paper entitled *The last stand of the steam engine*.[1] Electric motors used for haulage provide a higher energy-efficiency use than does coal burnt in the firebox of a locomotive but this has not resulted in a widespread conversion for the costs of electrifying a line are tremendous—in the pre-war Reading-Aldershot scheme of the S.R. £23,000 a route-mile was so spent—and there have to be particular advantages to warrant the conversion. The Weir Committee in 1931 estimated the capital cost of electrifying British railways at £261 million, excluding generating stations. In 1951 it was estimated that the minimum traffic density to warrant electrification in Britain was about 4 million trailing-ton-miles but by now the tonnage, to warrant the increased costs, is probably a quarter greater. It is estimated that in Britain there are about 3,000 route-miles along which the traffic density exceeds 5 million trailing-ton-miles. This is equal to about one-third of the routes which thus carry about two-thirds of the traffic. One advantage of electrification is that in place of the present haulage of 13 million tons of large locomotive coal used

[1] *Jour. Amer. Inst. Elect. Eng.*

in Britain under one-third of this quantity of lower grade coal would suffice and the length of haul would be less.

French experience has shown that one ton of poor quality coal in an electric generating station can replace four tons of large coal in a locomotive firebox and that one electric locomotive replaces three steam locomotives and one electrician two mechanics so the incentive to conversion may be great.

Electricity is of particular value in providing a quick service with frequent stops for motors have rapid acceleration, in operating steep gradients, in the working of long tunnels where ventilation is a problem and in providing an alternative to dear coal. Frequently a particular electrification scheme has been advantageous for two or more of these reasons. The Manchester–Sheffield electrification was undertaken because of the difficulties of working Woodhead tunnels and because of the heavy traffic, particularly of coal being carried to the industries of Lancashire ; freight locomotives, using 1,500 volts D.C., can handle 850-ton loose-coupled trains. The monthly saving, following the inauguration in September, 1954, was £28,000 and the full economies are not yet realized.

Electrification, with its advantages of acceleration compared with steam, has permitted intensive suburban services such as operate round London. It was to cope with the required frequency of trains that the S.R. pressed ahead with electrification and by 1939 had converted 702 route miles on their system and this formed the most extensive electrified suburban network in the world.

Tunnels as long as the $9\frac{1}{3}$ miles of the St. Gotthard have been worked by steam but the pollution of the air led to operating difficulties. In South Africa to work the heavy trains on the lines from the coast to the veldt the locomotives are supplied with a reservoir of compressed air to prevent the crews being asphyxiated in the tunnels. Electricity was first adopted in 1895 for a main line in the U.S.A. to eliminate smoke in the Baltimore tunnel and, as a result of a bad accident in a smoke-filled New York tunnel in 1902, the Albany legislature ordained that by 1908 all passenger trains within New York City were to be worked exclusively by electricity : this resulted in the remodelling of the Central Station. With underground lines, other than the shallow cut-and-cover of the Metropolitan in London, steam is impossible. With some routes, such as the Circle line in Glasgow, cable operation has been tried but now all are electrically worked, for the services required, with frequent trains and many stops, are best provided by the electric motor.

Long, steep gradients punish a steam locomotive by making a heavy drain on the boiler and on many mountainous sections it is necessary to provide three or more locomotives to deal with a train that can be easily handled by one on normal gradients. A suitable electric locomotive, such as those on the St. Gotthard line, can handle a 500-ton train up 20 miles of 1 in 40 at a steady speed of 40 m.p.h. Furthermore, it is possible by regenerative braking, by which the descent under the pull of gravity drives the motors as though they were dynamos, to feed back current into the conductor system.

To countries lacking resources of suitable coal, electricity can obviate the need to import provided there are sites to generate hydro-electricity. Steep gradients and a constant supply of water, whether from the natural flow of the rivers or from artificial lakes, are essential. Industrialized countries, such as France, Sweden and Switzerland, which have to import all or most of their coal supply, have turned to electrification using water-power to work long stretches of their railways: Switzerland, the most extreme case, has 96 per cent of her train miles electrically worked. At pre-war prices the conversion of the Swiss railways meant a capital cost of £30 million: the interest on this had to be earned by either economies in the working or by increased traffic. Water-power may be abundant but the utilization of it demands heavy expenditure.

EUROPEAN ELECTRIFIED SYSTEMS, 1952
(U.I.C. Internal Railway Statistics)

	Italy	France	Germany	Britain
Route-miles, '000	10·5	25·7	18·9	19·3
Electrified route-miles, % of total	34·4	10·4	5·8	4·8
Train-miles, million ...	122·3	233·4	317·6	376·4
Train-miles, electric, % of total	52·5	24·0	9·3	13·0

Availability of electric locomotives is considerable at 23 hours a day, compared with 10 hours with steam, and with multiple units the loss of time by shunting is eliminated. The Netherlands Railways in 1953 carried 71 per cent of the passenger traffic by electric power (saving annually 650,000 tons of coal), but although steam was abandoned for passenger haulage in 1955, and will be for freight in 1958, diesel-power is being used for the final conversion as the density of traffic does not warrant electrification.

Long distance electrification was adopted by 1917 for 440 miles of route on the Chicago, Milwaukee, St. Paul and Pacific R.R. to reduce working costs over three summit banks between Harlowton (Mont.) and Avery (Idaho). It was found that 42 electric locomotives did the work of 112 steam locomotives and was sufficiently successful to justify electrification in 1920 of the remaining 207 miles from Othello to Tacoma (Wash.).

Electrification has mainly taken place with 1,500 volts D.C. (or a lower voltage with third-rail), but the French railway administration is now using 25,000 volts A.C. and thereby avoids expensive transformers and also can use cheaper conductors.

Battery locomotives, the most successful the Drumm Battery, have been tried and offer the advantage of not requiring expensive lineside conductors. Battery railcars operate, at a maximum speed of 55 m.p.h. over several thousand route-miles in Germany. While they can run for 160 miles on one charge and can seat 78 passengers peak services have to be catered for by the conventional steam locomotive at an operating cost of three times that of the battery railcar. Their main advantage would seem to be for the branch line with a light traffic density.

DIESEL OPERATION

Petrol engines have been tried on the railway but they are not so satisfactory for heavy haulage as the diesel unit. The diesel, with its qualities of reliability and freedom from problems of water-supply and firing, has become the great rival to the steam locomotive. The factor which held back the adoption was the need to reduce the speed of the motor to that required for the wheels. A mechanical clutch, such as is used on a lorry, can be provided for small shunting units but for the massive express unit an alternative has to be sought. One device is to use an electrical link and the first diesel-electric units were developed in Germany and in Canada. As early as 1933 the *Flying Hamburger* averaged 77 m.p.h. between Berlin and Hamburg. The first light-weight diesel-electric unit used in the U.S.A. was the *Pioneer Zephyr* in 1934 and the following year the first diesel-electric locomotive in the U.S.A. was delivered to the Baltimore and Ohio R.R.; it weighed 126 short tons and out-hauled steam locomotives weighing 263 tons.

As oil has a higher energy value than its weight in coal and as there is no need to carry water (except for supplying a steam heating system), the range of a diesel engine is much longer than that of a steam. American experience suggests that one ton of fuel oil used in a diesel-electric locomotive does the work of about $9\frac{1}{2}$ tons of coal and this has greatly reduced operating costs. Furthermore the diesel can run longer than the steam both in daily duty and before it requires a major overhaul. It would have been impossible for a steam locomotive to have run non-stop between Chicago and Denver as was done with an experimental diesel run at 83·3 m.p.h. Faster services are helped by the great saving in servicing time. The operating costs per mile run are lower than with a steam locomotive and the diesel can work more hours in the day, with crews changing, but in Britain they are three to four times as expensive to construct. Possibly the diesel has a shorter life although against this must be offset its daily work which may be taken as three times that of a steam locomotive. Partial introduction of diesels is not very satisfactory because they need trained operatives and properly equipped workshops for maintenance.

Diesel operation of expresses was adopted before the war in Germany, Denmark, Siam, Algeria, the United States, Russia and Canada and the 1930s were years in which the diesel was tested in many environments. In Britain they first found a niche for shunting duties and post-war conditions would seem to justify their use for fast freight services (with adequately braked stock) and for passenger services where the traffic density does not warrant electrification. The diesel has the advantage that the capital costs may be more directly related to the work done than is possible with electrification.

Diesel operation offers many advantages. The motor can accelerate a train smoothly and rapidly for it has not the heavy reciprocating gear of the steam locomotive. Again the diesel-electric unit can exert its full horse-power at 10 m.p.h. whereas its steam rival is not fully effective until 40 m.p.h. This means that with frequent curves, which limit speeds, and with many changes of grade the load of a steam-hauled train is more restricted than with a diesel: on the Schreiber Division of the C.P.R., along the north shore of Lake Superior, train tonnage has been increased from 1,660 to 3,150 tons by using two-unit diesel-electrics and thereby nearly doubled the line capacity or halved the number of trains required. The ability to couple units together, shared with electric propulsion, allows the power to be adjusted to the traffic demands and does not add to the train-crew as occurs when a steam train is double-headed.

Adoption of diesel operation has been encouraged by their independence of water supply. The Rhodesian Railways, although they have plentiful supplies of coal at Wankie, 500 miles away, are using diesels for the Umtali-Salisbury section because water is scarce and it is only 200 miles from the fuel import point of Beira. There are drawbacks to the use of diesels. On long down-grades braking is a problem as wheels can heat and brake-blocks burn out but with diesel-electrics the wheels are allowed to drive the motors and the current generated is dissipated from heat-grids on the roof. In cold countries it is necessary to heat passenger trains and Canadian railway operators have found that on trans-continental trains 9,000 lb. of steam an hour must be produced and this requires water transport which is not easy to fit in economically within the diesel unit.

Although in Britain very large diesel-electric units have been made for the Argentine and other foreign lines the models for use in Britain, other than experimental, have hitherto been limited to smaller types suitable for shunting and have frequently been diesel-mechanical. The experimental models have been tested against a gas-turbine unit which may yet be evolved into a serious rival. Certain of the American "coal-lines" have experimented with coal-burning gas-turbine, for example, the

F

Pennsylvania R.R. in 1946, but they were not sufficiently successful and this company by 1949, within 30 months of trying its first diesel-electric, had one-third of its motive power in diesel units. In 1949 nearly one-third of the United States freight ton-miles and nearly one-half of the passenger car-miles were diesel-electric hauled. With the programme announced in 1955 British Railways may produce as rapid a transformation. The previous year the first British light-wight multiple diesel trains were introduced and the traffic increase in the West Riding was phenomenal and encouraging. In order to heat these trains oil-fired boilers to raise steam are provided.

The adoption of diesel power has been the salvation of American railways. In the 1930s many companies were in a state of bankruptcy and either had to reduce operating costs or abandon the works. The Monon railroad, with steep grades and weak bridges, could not introduce very heavy steam locomotives to haul heavier trains and the economies realized when diesel-electrics were tried as an expediency were startling. Under American Trade Union agreements 100 miles is regarded as a day's work and this means that in five hours with an express passenger train, or eight hours with a freight, a train crew can earn two or more "basic-day's" wages.

The speed of adoption was phenomenal and in 1946 United States railway companies ordered 802 diesel-electric units but only 48 steam despite considerable improvement in the design of the steam locomotive to counter this attraction towards diesels. Now no steam locomotives are manufactured in the U.S.A. At some centres a nucleus of steam locomotives was kept as a standby in case of failure of oil supplies but men cannot be found to go back to the rigours of footplate work.

MOTIVE POWER ON U.S. CLASS I RAILWAYS

	1939		1950	
	No.	Aver T.E.	No.	Aver T.E.
Steam	41,117	50,395	25,640	57,075
Electric	843	55,661	788	59,713
Diesel-electric units	510	?	14,047	57,487
Other types ...	41	?	19	?

T.E. = Tractive effort in lb.

In Australia shortage of water and dependence on poor local coals has encouraged the adoption of diesel-electric haulage and although, because of different service demands, the cost of 102·29*d*. for 1,000 gross ton-miles on the Trans-Australian line with diesel-electric operation cannot be exactly compared with 553·74*d*. on the Central Australia line with steam operation it, nevertheless, shows that there is a very considerable financial advantage.

At the moment diesel operation, particularly diesel-electric, appears to be the dominant agent but conditions are likely to change. If the cost of fuel oil becomes too high, other media, such as the gas-turbine or the electric motor fed from a conductor, are likely to become more advantageous, while a sign of the times is the announcement that some American companies are considering, as a long-term policy, experiments with locomotives driven by atomic energy.

CHAPTER VI

THE RAILWAY RETICULE

BEFORE the war there were 788,672 miles of railway in the world divided as follows : Americas 46·9 per cent of the total, Europe 32·6, Asia 10·9, Africa 5·6, Australasia 4·0.

The United States has about 29 per cent of the world's mileage and more railway mileage than South America, Asia, Africa and Australia combined. Most of the world's railway mileage was provided in the nineteenth century but active construction is still proceeding in some areas, particularly in Asia : in the last forty years the mileage in the U.S.S.R. territory has been increased by nearly fifty per cent while in China great additions are being made to the rudimentary system which existed before the war. While lines are being constructed in some countries the emphasis in western Europe and the United States has been on removing lines which have become redundant either through changes in the economy of a region or from the growth of rival transport services. Undoubtedly there had been an over-liberal provision of lines in the countries which had a network provided by private enterprise but even in some nationally controlled systems the routes provided, possibly for political reasons, were sometimes excessive and could not be maintained. The network is being made more reasonable and the services provided on it are being modernized.

The intensity of the railway network can be measured either by the mileage per 1,000 square miles of territory or by the mileage per 10,000 persons. Both approaches are subject to misunderstanding because the former may appear as grossly inadequate mileage for a continent such as Australia. With the measurement by number of persons a densely settled country, such as Belgium, may appear less well served than it is in practice. Relating to population is the slightly more useful approach as it does give some indication of the traffic possibilities, assuming that there is a modicum of traffic per head of population which will go by rail. Figure 3 has been prepared by plotting the mileage per 1,000 square miles against the mileage per 10,000 persons. In practice it is not possible to sub-divide each country so that the boundaries of the physiographic units can be taken for calculations of the railway density. Although economic development frequently over-rides the relief nevertheless within a zone of similar economic situation the physiographic factors dominate the pattern.

The effectiveness of cover may be shown by distance from a railway station, allowance being made for obstacles, such as bridgeless rivers, which may prevent access. For general maps the distance from the railway line, and not the station, may be taken as a measure of the territory served and Figure 4 shows for the world the areas more than about twenty miles from a railway. Twenty miles is an arbitrary distance but it does indicate the districts which may be regarded as so remote that the cost of haulage to a railing point is a definite handicap on transport of products. Such districts so remote from railways are not usually well provided with all-weather roads. The growth of the railway network is also suggested on this map by the stippling which is applied to districts which in 1875 were more than about twenty miles from a railway but now no longer have that handicap. The considerable area of such districts in territories of the southern hemisphere and North America, all of which are now zones of activity in farming or mining industry, emphasizes that outwith western Europe and the eastern States of the U.S.A. the railway is a comparative newcomer. In considering the economic development of the past 80 years careful attention must be paid to the growth of rail facilities.

The physical factors in relation to the provision of the network are considered below by continents and special reference is made to the areas of difficulty. The treatment is not uniform between the different continents; southern Africa is discussed with more detail than Latin America partly because of its interest as showing the activity of various colonial powers and partly because railway construction is still a major factor in the exploitation of mineral resources. Western Europe and North America, on the other hand, have long achieved their intricate

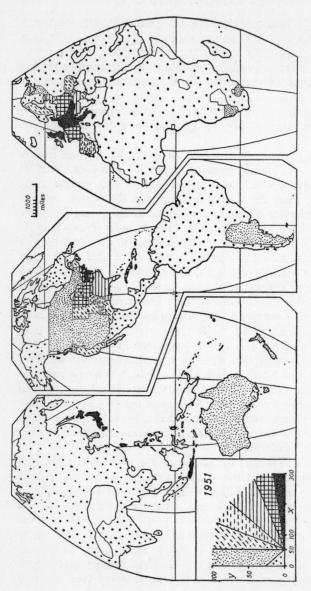

FIG. 3. RAIL DENSITY, 1951

The scale is given for the densities obtained by plotting x (mileage per '000 square miles) against y (mileage per 10,000 persons). Administrative territories without railways are shown without any shading. The two lower "zones", stippled, are those where railway facilities may be regarded as below "normal" and are due to either slight population or great areas without an appreciable railway mileage.

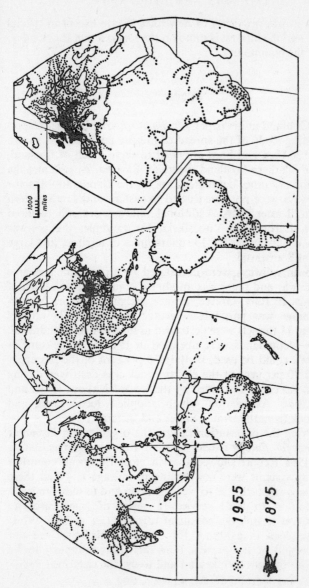

FIG. 4. RAIL COVERAGE, 1875 AND 1955

The width of the lines and dots approximates to 20 miles on the scale of the map. The comparative recent introduction of railways emphasizes how the flows of traffic have been stimulated since 1875.

railway network, provision of new lines is rare except in special instances, and the interest is more on the services that the railways render to the community.

EUROPE

Sven Godlund in his paper *Ein Innovationsverlauf in Europa*,[1] an interesting study of the spread of railway facilities, has shown that by 1836 they had been provided to serve much of England, Wales and southern Scotland, Belgium, Bavaria, Austria and the Lyon region of France but that, except for the Leningrad–Moscow area, railways were not constructed in eastern and south-eastern Europe until after 1856. Additional railways are still required in eastern Europe; in Yugoslavia, for example, the pre-war mileage was only 1 mile for 13 square miles of territory and large areas are still unserved.

European railways were devastated to an incredible degree during the war and there was an almost complete breakdown of the systems. In Italy, Greece, France, Belgium and the Netherlands damage was particularly acute: in Greece 379 railway bridges and 11 tunnels were destroyed in the German withdrawal. When the Netherlands were liberated in 1945 only one-third of the network could be used. In Italy 56 per cent of the passenger stock and 90 per cent of the electric track was destroyed during hostilities. Recovery was aided by the United Nations Relief and Rehabilitation Association which supplied locomotives and rolling stock from the United States and Britain.

Following the devastation of war the organization *Economic Commission for Europe* issued reports on the transport situation and the 1953 Report showed that in most European countries the railway systems were contracting in mileage and that there was an increasing turnover to electrification and to diesel railcars.

In addition to local services a series of trans-European services serves to link the continent together (*see* p. 154). While these have been in existence for many decades they are not immutable and at the present time this trans-European traffic is tending to by-pass Switzerland and to use the electrified Paris–

[1] *Lund Studies in Geography.* Ser. B., No. 6, 1952.

Lyon–Modane route; as a counter-measure Swiss financiers are aiding the electrification of French lines leading to Basle.

The regional description which follows is based on a compromise between the major physical units and the political units; while it would be useful to consider, for example, the North European Plain as a unit for the provision of railways, nevertheless the political frontiers have so often over-ridden geographical considerations that the compromise solution has been adopted.

British Isles

The railway reticule in the British Isles was woven finely and there are many routes which could not now be justified. Although there was no attempt to follow a plan the richness of the London traffic resulted in most of the large English companies radiating from the metropolis. This emphasis upon London was not foreseen in the early days when much of the finance of the pioneer lines came from Liverpool. A number of important English companies did not have their own metals into the metropolis and among these may be instanced the Lancashire and Yorkshire Railway and the North Eastern Railway. One company, which had for long remained as a provincial line, was the Manchester, Sheffield and Lincolnshire Railway, towards the close of the last century; it added to its routes the line from Nottingham *via* Rugby to London and became the last of the trunk routes to be built.

The lines to the south and into East Anglia, crossing districts without coal, developed suburban and holiday traffic and also strove to acquire a share of the packet trade to the continent. The other lines reached out to coalfields of South Wales, the Midlands, and northern England and, in addition to carrying coal to the metropolis, also served industrial developments which in Victorian times were dependent upon mining. Beyond the boundaries of England lay the important centres of Dublin, Belfast, Glasgow and Edinburgh and the companies improved the track to allow them to compete with each other. To the desire to obtain a share of the valuable trunk traffic may be attributed great engineering feats which would not have been warranted by local needs—the Britannia tubular bridge, the harbours at Holyhead and Heysham, the Royal Border Bridge at Berwick, and the many miles of well-graded route may be instanced as the types of work on which many millions of pounds were spent. There were cross-country routes and the main obstacle to these, the Pennines, is referred to elsewhere in its effect on railway construction (p. 44).

In Scotland the principal problems for the engineer have been the high relief and the great estuaries. The crossing of the Southern Uplands has been aided by the presence of connecting valleys, for example the Nith and the Clyde or the Teviot and the Gala, but even with these the gradients affect train haulage. North of the geological structure known as the Highland Line routes penetrate—along the east coast, by the Tay valley and, in the west by minor valleys. Two lines, both partly financed by government loans, reach out to the west coast north of Fort William and it is unfortunate that their termini are so close together when Ullapool could have been used instead of Kyle of Lochalsh and thus have spread more widely the value of a railway connection. It is interesting that an "obvious" gap, that followed by the Caledonian Canal, has no railway, although there were several schemes, and this is a sign of its poverty for traffic. North of Inverness the single track line which pursues an erratic route was largely financed by the then Duke of Sutherland and could never have been an economic proposition except in time of war when naval supplies are carried north for shipment to Scapa Flow base.

In Ireland railway construction was encouraged by the local authorities when it was realized that the traffic resources did not entice the private investor. Many light railways were built in an endeavour to match the low revenue but these lines have largely been abandoned with road competition. The partition has cut across the natural flow of traffic between Belfast and the Republic's capital.

Low Countries

Belgium was the first country to plan its railway system from the beginning and not rely upon the junction of lines of local interest. In 1835 services were inaugurated upon the line from Brussels to Malines and it was the first continental line to employ steam locomotives. The Netherlands followed a year later with the line from Amsterdam to Haarlem but, unlike Belgium, there was no national plan ; the first line was, for example, on a gauge of 6 ft. 4½ in. Although a region without high relief there are grading problems and the descent at 1 in 32 from Ans down to Liége, in the incised valley of the Meuse, was at first worked by cable. The route from Brussels *via* Arlon to the Luxembourg frontier was badly built by private enterprise and is a succession of switchbacks. There is the problem of bridges across the Maas, Yssel, Neder-Rhine and Hollandsch Diep : for example the Moerdijk Bridge is 5,000 ft. long and there are in the Netherlands 15 bridges of 1,200 ft. or more in length. In order to maintain river navigation long, rising approach embankments are required.

The Belgian density of railways, by area, is the greatest in the world and about double that of the Netherlands. In the latter country the railway pattern is dominated by the cross-lines Amsterdam to Eindhoven and Rotterdam to Arnhem. The average travelling distances are low, in the Netherlands only 25 miles, and a fast and frequent service is required which is not suited to the slow acceleration of steam locomotives.

Since 1884 many light railways were provided and while these have largely succumbed to road competition some, such as the Belgian coastal line, have been electrified and retain traffic. Two world wars have raged across Belgium and devastated the railway system : after 1918 350 important bridges and one tunnel had to be reconstructed and comparable damage had to be repaired in 1945.

France

Railway construction in France was sluggish in starting while the Government considered a plan of radial lines focusing on Paris. Concessions were given to companies but in 1878 a group of bankrupt companies was taken over by the State and for long these lines were known for their inefficiency. In 1937 the Societé Nationale des Chemins de Fer Français was formed with the State holding 51 per cent of the capital and since then there has been a remarkable resurgence of the system although the railways are run at a financial loss. Some lines are being electrified, about 125 miles a year, and for others diesel operation is being adopted ; no steam locomotives have been ordered since 1952. Electrification began with the desire to use French hydro-electricity generated in the Pyrenees or the Alps, instead of importing coal, but now it is being extended to the north-east, using 25,000 volts A.C., to haul the heavy coke and iron-ore traffic between Valenciennes and Thionville. In 1945 traffic could be carried on only 11,125 miles out of a pre-war mileage of 26,500 and during the restoration the opportunity was taken to improve the layout; for example, at Orléans where a new marshalling yard and avoiding lines were provided.

There are regions of France where the relief has been responsible for elaborate structures. The deeply dissected valleys of the Massif Central are difficult to cross; the Fades viaduct over the gorge of the Sioule needed deep foundations for its lofty piers, the Garabit viaduct across the Truyère has a great central arch of 541 ft. span rising 401 ft. above the water, while the Viaur viaduct, 1,345 ft. long, between Rodez and Albi crosses a gorge, with a main span of 722 ft. The lines crossing the Pyrenees, other than the coastal routes, are modern because of the heavy works. The Somport tunnel, between Pau and Zaragoza, was not opened until 1928. The slope on the French side of the mountains is steeper than on the Spanish and thus the maximum gradients on the Somport line are 1 in 23 in France and 1 in 50 in Spain.

Another region of difficult relief is the French Alps. In the northern sector a great longitudinal sill valley fronts the massifs and this allows better graded and more effective routes than occurs with the rudimentary network of the Southern Alps where large areas are over ten miles from a railway.

Germany and Central Europe

From the glaciated lowlands of the North European Plain to the high fold mountains of the Alps extend numerous railways. Much of the pattern is laid out in response to the needs of the German and Austro-Hungarian Empires but there has been later modification of the network with the creation of new States from the dismemberment of the old. Partition raises many problems and not least among these is the disruption of the previous flows of traffic.

Across the Alpine fold mountains run a number of rail routes (*see* p. 46) and the severity of these must not just be measured by the length of the one summit tunnel but account must also be taken of the ancillary works which added greatly to the expense. When at the beginning of this century the Imperial Railways of Austria-Hungary were opening the new route from Linz to Trieste, apart from the 5·1 miles of the Tauern tunnel, were many formidable tunnels—Karawanken (26,167 ft.), Wocheiner (20,801 ft.), Bosruck (15,650 ft.) to mention only those over a mile long. The most difficult section was that between the Baca and Isonzo valleys which required numerous bridges and viaducts and minor tunnels: Salcano Bridge, a masonry structure over the Isonzo river, has a 279-ft.-long central arch rising 118 ft. above the water.

Railways came early into this then non-industrial region of Europe: the first line was the horse-drawn railway from Vienna to Raab, opened in 1828, the Nuremberg and Fürth line opened in 1835, the first trunk line, Leipzig to Dresden, opened in 1839 and later the first Swiss line, from Zurich to Baden, opened in 1847. In 1841 an Austrian engineer was sent to the United States to study the construction and working of the Baltimore and Ohio R.R. and he reported that a locomotive-operated line could be worked over the Semmering Pass and this became, when it was opened in 1854, the first European mountain railway of any importance. In 1951 a new tunnel was opened, parallel to the old, to cope with increased traffic.

As well as the mountains the broad rivers and ill-drained glacial trenches offer an obstacle to construction. The Rhine was first bridged at Cologne about 1850 by an orthodox type of bridge but even so late as 1865 a bridge of boats was installed at Maximiliansau for a railway: light locomotives were used but their weight was sufficient to depress the sections of the bridge and the passage was made constantly up a slope.

Some of the routes carry a significance greater than their national value because they form links for trans-European services and this is particularly true of the main lines in Switzerland and Austria.

Scandinavian countries

Denmark with a small area and slight relief offers less obstacles to the railway engineer than the other Scandinavian countries but there has been the difficulty of the fragmentation into islands with the result that ferry-boats have long been used to be replaced, in a number of cases, by long bridges. In addition to the main lines there are many local lines of value for the beet and other agricultural activities. Railways in Denmark have been responsible for changes in the relative importance of towns, the railway for example created the port of Esbjerg, and a valuable review of their influence is that by Aage Aagesen.[1]

Norway and Sweden face the problem of great distances and the dissection of the valleys which either have to be rounded or crossed by massive bridges. Norway is more handicapped than Sweden because of the steepness of the uplands and the absence of a continuous lowland along its much indented coast. A further disadvantage is that the route of the expensive railway which is being built from Trondheim to Bodö is paralleled by efficient shipping services and, even if these are reduced in number, the the navigational aids must be maintained.

The narrow-gauge line to serve a coalmine at Ny-Ålesund in Spitsbergen has the distinction of being the most northerly railway in the world.

Sweden has more sources of revenue for her railways and the iron-mines provide a bulk commodity which suits railway operating. For strategic reasons the inland line to the north was completed during this century. A line rounds the head of the Gulf of Bothnia but, because Finland has the wider Russian gauge, through trains cannot be run. The railway network of Finland had its essential framework laid down to suit Russian strategic needs but, after the creation of the Republic, many new lines have had to be built, including some made necessary by the surrender of territory to Russia after the Second World War.

Eastern Europe

In eastern Europe the network becomes more sparse and this is partly to be explained by the physical obstacles of the Carpathians and the Pripet Marshes but it is more the reflection of belated industrial development. The first Russian railway was opened from St. Petersburg to the suburbs in 1837, with a gauge

[1] *Geografiske studier over jernbanerne i Danmark*, København, 1949.

of 6 ft., but the first trunk line, that connecting Moscow and
St. Petersburg, was in use by 1851, up to which time Russia
only had 370 miles of railways. This line has a ruling grade of
1 in 1,660 and is so straight that the rail-distance is only seven
miles longer than the straight-line distance. The 'sixties and the
early 'seventies were years of railway boom in Russia.

After the damage caused during the Revolution and the Civil
War the Soviet Government embarked upon new construction
which opened the Ukraine and mining areas to further development but, despite these additions, the mileage is still slight in
relation to either the population or the area.

South-eastern Europe

Many of the railways in this region were constructed to meet
the strategic needs of the Austro-Hungarian or Turkish Empires
and cross-links to meet commercial demands are still required.
Wars and disturbance of political boundaries have reoriented
the traffic and the thought, for example, that Salonika might
become the port to serve the northern Balkans has never been
realized. After 1918 the newly created Yugoslavia was faced with
the necessity of evolving a national network which would open
the port of Split to trade with the interior. Following the Second
World War there has been a fresh resurgence of railway construction while the neighbouring State of Albania has, in this
period, acquired its first lines. Narrow-gauge lines, mostly 2 ft. 6 in.
gauge, are important in Yugoslavia and the most valuable of
these is the line Belgrade–Sarajevo–Dubrovnik–Titograd (530
miles). Heavy engineering is required in the Balkans particularly
in crossing the Balkan Range. Another difficulty experienced
in the Balkans is crossing ill-drained alluvial flats which alternate
frequently with rocky ridges. With paucity of traffic railway
construction makes a heavy burden on the national exchequers.

Italy

The first line opened in Italy was that in 1839 from Naples to
Portici (5 miles). Extension of the system was hindered by the
political disturbances following Garibaldi's conquest of Naples
in 1860. In northern Italy the lines were built to suit the strategic
needs of Austria. During their history the railways of Italy have

been nationalized, returned to private companies and re-nationalized. The inter-war period saw a renaissance which, up to that date, was the most remarkable in the world. New routes were then opened, for example, the direct line between Florence and Bologna, which reduced the rail distance from 82 to 60½ miles at a cost of £12 million: the high cost was due to the boring of 30 tunnels aggregating 23 miles. Shorter distance and easier gradients reduced the journey time from 2½ to 1 hour. Another direct line was that connecting Rome with Naples which, when it was opened in 1927, reduced the journey time from 4½ to 2¾ hours.

War damage was very heavy in Italy and in 1945 it was impossible to travel directly between any two Italian cities except Genoa and Milan.

Iberia

The early railways of Spain were constructed with British advice, but, owing to unfortunate experiences over payment of some British contractors, little British capital was sunk into Spanish construction. The gauge of 5 ft. 6 in. was selected for technical and not strategic reasons as is usually stated. Railway construction is still proceeding and in 1933 the line from Zaragoza to Caminreal was built to link with the Somport tunnel across the central Pyrenees. After the Civil War work began on a crossing of the wild terrain between Madrid and Burgos and this demanded heavy engineering including the large and high Lozoya Viaduct which has an unusual design to allow spate water to escape. Portugal is linked with Spain by several routes but the principal traffic artery is that connecting Lisbon and Oporto.

ASIA

The railway pattern of this continent is dominated by the mountain core and by the desire to penetrate towards the interior from the seaboards and from the broad front with Europe. Surface rivals to the rail are few, apart from sea transport, because all the rivers which flow north to the Arctic Ocean are frozen in winter and have extensive floods as the upper reaches melt before the mouths. Most of the railway development, apart from that of the U.S.S.R. and Japan, has resulted from foreign capital and within the various spheres of influence the description will be by large regions.

Northern Asia

This territory is taken as that north of the high fold mountains and includes therefore a great variety of environments from hot to cold deserts and from steppe land to dense coniferous forests. The major unit in the railway facilities is the Trans-Siberian line which links Moscow to Vladivostock.[1] The inspiration for this line came from the success of the Canadian Pacific transcontinental line and it was opened throughout in 1904. A problem of the engineers was building great bridges; there are eight each over 1,000 ft., built without transport facilities to carry heavy girders. A ferry service was used to cross Lake Baikal until the route round the south end of the lake, which required 38 tunnels in 42 miles, was completed. A spur of the line was constructed across Manchuria which saved 600 miles compared with the route keeping to the Russian bank of the Amur. The gauge was 5 ft. with a huge loading gauge, but the original rails weighed only 54 lb. to the yard and, with the single track and wood-fuel, resulted in slow trains. The outbreak of the Russo-Japanese war in 1904 emphasized the strategic value of this line. From this spinal line, which is now double track throughout, the Soviet Government have built key lines particularly into the Kirghiz and Turkistan regions—the Turksib line was opened in 1930—and have connected in this way the Ural industrial region with the Kuzbas coalfield and with the food- and cotton-producing districts. These lines also have a strategic significance in that they make an easier approach to India and Tibet. In 1954 an announcement was made about new lines being constructed from the Trans-Siberian line across Mongolia to China and, following the Old Silk Road, across Sinkiang. It is also reported that, in addition to the second Siberian railway which will run from the Karaganda coalfield and is to cross the first Siberian line at Irkutsk on its way to Soviet Harbour, a strategic line is planned north-eastwards to the Bering Strait.

[1] For an early account of a journey by this route see M. M. Shoemaker, *The Great Siberian Railway*, New York, 1903.

China and Manchuria

The first railway in China was a short 2 ft. 6 in. gauge line opened in 1875 to connect the coalmine at Woosung with Shanghai: unauthorized by the Government it was purchased after an accident and destroyed. Five years later a horse-drawn railway was opened to serve coalmines and in 1886 the Kaipung coalfield was connected with Taku by a standard-gauge track. In 1900 there were only 300 miles of railway but ten years later 5,200. After the Sino-Japanese War of 1894 it was thought that the Empire was breaking-up and there was a rush to obtain railway concessions. British, French, Belgian, German, Russian, Portuguese, American and Japanese capital became available and resulted in the early twentieth-century flush of construction. From 1896 there have been at least ten major military or political upheavals which have hindered the provision and working of railways in China. Under the present Government plans have been announced to extend the railway system to give a complete linkage from Indo-China northwards to Korea and from the China Sea westwards to Mongolia and Sinkiang. A strategic line, completed in 1955, is that linking Amoy and Quemoy with the Shanghai–Canton trunk line: it will be of value as a route towards Formosa.

Manchuria first had important railways from Russia and the gauge used was 5 ft. but when the Japanese obtained control the Russian-built lines were converted to 4 ft. $8\frac{1}{2}$ in. Without railways Dairen could never have obtained the commercial significance that it did; freight traffic on the South Manchurian Railway rose from 1·3 million tons in 1907–8 to 18·9 million in 1933–4, which reflected the railway's influence on cash-cropping and industrial development.

Japan

The first railway in Japan, from Tokyo to Yokohama, was constructed in 1872 as a relief measure for a rice famine. At first the provision of railways was sluggish but the years 1894–8 were the Japanese railway mania years, when many miles were planned by both State and private enterprise. Japan often presents extremely difficult terrain for construction and steep grades and tunnels abound. The gauge of most lines is 3 ft. 6 in. but there is a project for a standard-gauge longitudinal line to provide faster connections in the main island. One of the greatest modern improvements has been the undersea tunnel, opened in 1942, linking Shimonoseki and Moji.

Earthquakes are a problem for railway maintenance. On October 28th, 1911, in the district round Nagoya and Gefu the works were almost completely destroyed; bridges were wrecked, rails bent and stations became rubble. The September, 1923, earthquake did similar damage in the Tokyo district. Electrification has been adopted on over a thousand miles of route, partly because of the hydro-electric power available and partly because on lines with many tunnels, for example that from Hachioji to Kofu, it eases the working.

South-eastern Asia

The railway network has been mainly provided by colonial powers to aid the shipment of plantation crops. There is now a linkage by metre-gauge lines from Singapore through Malaya to northern Thailand. During the war, to meet Japanese military needs, the Burma-Siam line (*see* p. 26) and the Kra Isthmus line were constructed but they no longer exist as there was little commercial value and maintenance was difficult.

Indonesia

Java is more densely populated than Belgium and has a route mileage of only 2,936 miles yet this is great compared with that of its larger neighbour Sumatra, 877 miles. The first lines were not opened until the 'seventies and since then have proved of considerable value in encouraging plantation cropping and the working of the Sumatran coal. Although Java is a mountainous island it is only in the west, in the Preanger country, that gradients are steep but there are numerous sharp curves and viaducts over deep ravines. Before the war the fastest narrow-gauge runs in the world were on the Java Railway but, after an accident when a water-buffalo on the line derailed a train with a loss of 25 lives, there was no night running.

India, Pakistan, Burma and Ceylon

The first railway in India was that from Bombay to Thana, opened in 1853, and within the century over 40,000 miles of route had been provided. At first expansion was slow and by 1880 the mileage was under 9,000. The network was based on Lord Dalhousie's recommendation that the centres of Bombay, Calcutta, Madras and Lahore should be the framework.[1] Most of the important lines were built on 5 ft. 6 in. gauge, but there was a subsidiary network of narrower gauges (metre, 2 ft. 6 in. and 2 ft.) and there are 31 points in northern India and 22 in southern India where trans-shipment, with consequent loss of time and damage occurs and it is planned to provide a metre-gauge link from Khandwa to Hingoli which will join more firmly the northern and southern narrow-gauge systems. The political partition of the peninsula reoriented the flow of traffic and has required the building of new lines to avoid crossing political boundaries.

The first line built in Ceylon was from Colombo to Kandy to help the export of coffee. In the mountainous country steep gradients and sharp curves make rail travel slow and some sections have been abandoned. The summit point of the system is between Pattipola and Ohiya, 6,226 ft.

Because of the competition from navigation on the Irrawaddy the first Burmese line was not opened until 1877. Until 1934, when the Ava Bridge was built across the river near Mandalay, the north–south railway system was in two sections linked only by a ferry service. This bridge was only repaired after war damage in 1955 but the Gokteik Viaduct, which links the Shan States with Mandalay, was repaired by 1951.

South-western Asia

To link the shores of the Mediterranean with the Persian Gulf was long a dream of railway engineers. In 1856 a London company received a concession to construct a line parallel with the Euphrates but the concession lapsed and in 1888 a German syndicate received a concession for the Anatolian Railway. Not until 1940 were the works completed allowing through trains to run from the Bosporus to Baghdad. The most difficult sections were crossing the Taurus and Amanus Mountains, west and east of Adana, where numerous tunnels and lofty viaducts were

[1] A. C. O'Dell, "Some Geographical Aspects of Railways in India and Pakistan". *Indian Geog. Journ.*, 1951, pp. 189–95.

required and grades are steep. Lines have also been proposed from Haifa to Baghdad and from Jeddah, on the Red Sea, to Riyadh and thence, by the existing standard-gauge line to Dammam on the Persian Gulf.

Between the two world wars the Turkish railway network was greatly increased with emphasis on strategic lines towards the eastern frontier. Before World War II a syndicate constructed the Trans-Persia line from Bandarsharpur, on the Persian Gulf, to Bandarshah on the shores of the Caspian, with a branch from Tehran towards Tabriz, which had been reached since 1916 by a 5-ft. gauge Russian-built line. Construction, with over 140 long tunnels south of Tehran alone, was expensive, about £30 million, but this railway was opened in 1937, in time for the need to send supplies to Russia. There are summits north and south of Tehran and the worst of these is that over the Elburz Mountains which requires grades of 1 in 36 as it ascends in three great zig-zag curves to the Gaduk Summit, 6,929 ft. Operation during the Second World War was extremely difficult because the line was not laid out to handle daily imports of 10,000 tons and also the equipment, borrowed from other countries, was not always suitable, for example the injectors failed during hot weather. Diesels had to be introduced because it was found that, even with oil-burning to raise steam, crews were asphyxiated in the tunnels when trains were double-headed.

In 1908 the Hedjaz Railway from Damascus to Medina was opened (*see* p. 25) but owing to war damage the section south of Maan has been closed since 1915.[1] The Haifa branch of this line is unique in that for 50 miles it is below sea-level and at the bridge over the Jordan is 700 ft. below sea-level. Construction was extremely difficult in the Levant as was found when the Allied Military Forces laid the standard-gauge line along the coast between Acre and Beirut.

AFRICA

The African continent has very poor railway facilities and, unlike parts of South America, lacks continuously navigable

[1] In 1956 plans were announced for the restoration of this railway route.

waterways to supplement the rail routes. The variety of gauges makes the network less effective than the pattern would suggest as also does the light character of so much of the permanent way. Scattered widely over the continent, although it lacks the dizzy heights of an Andean system, there is the problem of surmounting steep slopes whether these be the edge of the plateau, close to the coast, or the fractured sides of a rift valley.

Railways came comparatively late to the continent: the first, Alexandria to Cairo, was opened in 1854. The period of real expansion was from late in the nineteenth century under the incentives of either mineral workings or politics. Cecil Rhodes suggested the longitudinal Cape-to-Cairo line and this caught the public fancy particularly as it was linked with the then current Imperialism. This spinal route is undoubtedly of local value but as the railhead pushed northwards from Cape Town so the mineral fields successively tapped gained less advantage and each in turn sought for a lateral escape from the long haul—the Rand to Durban and Lourenço Marques, the Rhodesias to Beira and Katanga to Lobito Bay. When the railhead reached the Copperbelt it was realized that the logical line of advance northwards was through the Belgian Congo and not through the more difficult terrain of the rift area of East Africa. It is unlikely that the rail-link will ever be completed between Cape and Cairo but as early as 1934[1] in a timetable of the Sudan Railways the following showed how the journey could be made by public-service vehicles:

Section	Miles	Transport
Alexandria–Cairo–Luxor–Shellal	685	Egyptian Railways (4 ft. 8½ in. Assuan-Shellal 2 ft. 5½ in.)
Shellal–Wadi Halfa	208	Nile steamer
Wadi Halfa–Khartoum–Kosti	817	Sudan Railways (3 ft. 6 in.)
Kosti–Juba	880	White Nile steamer
Juba–Nimule	122	Bus
Nimule–Pakwach	142	Nile steamer
Pakwach–Butiaba	58	Lake Albert steamer

[1] At the close of 1928 it became possible to travel by public-service vehicles from Cape Town to Egypt without leaving British or British-administered territory.

Section	Miles	Transport
Butiaba–Masindi Port	75	Bus
Masindi Port–Namasagali	106	Lake Kioga steamer
Namasagali – Kampala – Port Bell	125	East African Railways (metre)
Port Bell–Mwanza	271	Lake Victoria steamer
Mwanza – Tabora – Kigoma	470	East African Railways (metre)
Kigoma–Albertville	81	Lake Tanganyika steamer
Albertville–Kabalo	170	Upper Congo Railway (metre)
Kabalo–Bukama	353	Lualaba steamer
Bukama – Elisabethville – Sakania	442	Katanga Railway (3 ft. 6 in.)
Sakania–Cape Town	2,158	Rhodesian and South African Railways (3 ft. 6 in.)

The journey was slow—it took five days from Kabalo to Bukama alone—and so these connecting services were a negligible rival when public air transport commenced between north and south Africa in the late 1930s.

Before the advent of the heavy-duty road vehicle African economic development stood or fell on the construction of a rail link at minimum cost. Much of the railway pattern was located after the first surveys of the country were made by railway engineers and the lines meandered, taking advantage of every kloof and ridge, to gain altitude: the Hex River Pass, Montagu Pass and the Kei river valley routes may be instanced out of many examples. As traffic built-up over the years so these pioneer surface lines had to be re-aligned and reconstructed to heavier standards. Reversing loops and sinuosities are being eliminated by tunnels: for example, the Delville tunnel (3,002 ft.) on the important main line between Durban and Pietermaritzburg and another tunnel of 3,202 ft., for a time the longest in South Africa, on the East London–Springfontein line. Between Waterval Onder and Waterval Boven the original line, following the Elandspruit, rose 682 ft. in 3¾ miles and had a rack-operated section of 1 in 20 but, with expensive realignment, this has been reduced to 1 in 50. Today the correct approach to the problem is to provide all-weather roads to carry the initial burden and to postpone railway construction until the traffic warrants the provision of the more rigid rail linkage : in Nyasaland the Federal Government decided in 1954 to provide a road, instead of a railway, from railhead at Salima to Lilongwe and thus saved £0·9 million.

Discussion of the problems of different track and loading gauges was first begun officially for tropical Africa in 1926 by the Crown Agents for the Colonies. Although linkage was then an academic question, standards were laid down for track and rolling stock so that they could ultimately be interchangeable. The metre-gauge East African Railways were furthest from the average and in recent years all metre-gauge steel sleepers have been made convertible to 3 ft. 6 in. gauge and new structures have enlarged clearances while, after tests to verify that it was efficient at 9,000 ft. above sea-level, the automatic vacuum brake was adopted as standard.

Southern Africa

When railway construction commenced from Cape Town and Durban in 1859, the first line was opened in 1860 for the two miles from the wharf to Durban, 4 ft. 8½ in. gauge was adopted but when the plateau edge was reached the advantages of the cheaper and more flexible 3 ft. 6 in. gauge were realized and this became standard. At first extension was slow but expansion came in response to mining demands. Johannesburg was the Mecca of the rail race from the ports and by 1892 was connected with Lourenço Marques, Durban, East London, Port Elizabeth and, by a circuitous route, with Cape Town ; now Johannesburg is the great node of the southern network.

MILEAGE

Year	Route	Notes
1865	68	
1875	155	
1885	1,820	Opening of Kimberley diamond fields
1895	3,529	Opening of Rand goldfields
1910	7,575	Union of South Africa
1925	11,750	Includes 1,331 miles in S.W. Africa
1953	12,607 — 3 ft. 6 in. gauge	
	793 — 2 ft. gauge	

The spinal line which controls the pattern is that of Cape Town–De Aar–Kimberley–Mafeking–Bulawayo and, located as it is on the eastern limit of aridity, few lines run westwards but there is a considerable reticule to the east with gaps due to the reserved territories of Basutoland and Swaziland. The greatest westwards branch is from De Aar to Luderitz and Walvis Bay and it connects with the 2-ft. gauge Otavi line. This westward line was constructed largely for political and military purposes.

Since 1945 there has been very heavy capital expenditure to cope with the pressure of traffic and works have included the doubling of track, reduction of curves, longer passing-loops, boring of tunnels and electrification. By 1955 the two-mile tunnel between Lowlands and Hidcote in Natal was bored throughout: this, the longest tunnel in Africa, is part of the scheme to realign the route from Durban to Johannesburg. The South African Railways have not only to carry the traffic of the Union but also, *via* Mafeking and, to a much lesser extent, *via* Beitbridge, much of the traffic of the Rhodesias.

Rhodesias and Katanga

By 1897 Cecil Rhodes had pushed the railhead to Bulawayo and two years later the line was virtually completed from Beira into Salisbury with a climb at 1 in 40 to Eagle's Nest summit, 5,418 ft. This latter route eliminated the dependence on pack-animals which had made more difficult the ascent from the coastal belt to the 4,400 ft. of the plateau. Despite the Boer War the rail-heads of Salisbury and Bulawayo were linked in 1902 and the intention was to press north-north-east to the shores of Lake Tanganyika, but the discovery of coal at Wankie meant that the line was turned to enter Northern Rhodesia immediately down-stream of the Victoria Falls and, from there, the outlet was towards the Congo.

The Rhodesia Railways were purchased by the Government of Southern Rhodesia in 1947 and a curious anomaly is that the 580 miles between Vryburg and Bulawayo are owned by the Rhodesia Railways, but the Rhodesian locomotives are manned, and the trains worked, by the South African Railways. In the decade following the war coal output at Wankie trebled and the copper output doubled and this has necessitated, despite heavy

capital expenditure, considerable pressure on the rail capacity:
in 1955 one of the copper combines agreed to provide wagons
which could be hired to the Rhodesia Railways and so save the
nationalized concern from further capital problems when it was
already overburdened. The implementation of the Kariba hydro-
electric scheme will reduce the haulage of coal and coke to the
Copperbelt.

Rhodesia has outlets to Cape Town, Beira and Benguela and
the last is best suited as regards sea distance from north European
ports but, by the 1950 Lisbon Convention, it was agreed to maintain preferential rates in favour of Beira. If the West Nicholson
branch were extended to Beitbridge it would reduce the rail distance
of Bulawayo from an ocean port by 300 miles. Rhodesian opinion
prefers, largely because it would give a longer haul on Federal
metals, an extension already being constructed from Bannock-
burn, on the Shabani branch, along the north bank of the Lim-
popo and to cross on an irrigation barrage to Lourenço Marques.
One chord-line which would greatly improve the railway network,
and shorten the distance from the coppermines to Beira by 500
miles, is that from Kafue to Sinoia but the cost would be £20
million as it requires another great bridge across the Zambesi.

At Sakania the Rhodesian system connects with the Katanga
Railways of the Belgian Congo. Thanks to the energy of [Sir]
Robert Williams work began in 1903 on the Benguela Railway to
provide an outlet at Lobito Bay, undoubtedly the finest natural
harbour of Africa. This line, using the Lengue Gorge, ascends to
the high plateau and crosses it near the Congo–Zambesi water-
parting to link with the Katanga system. The relative distances
from Tenke, in Haut Katanga, show the advantages of Lobito Bay
for haulage but the traffic, although increasing, is not so great as
the distance advantage would suggest.

TENKE TO SOUTHAMPTON

| | Miles | |
Via	Rail	Sea
Beira	1,776	7,574
Cape Town	2,463	5,978
Lobito Bay	1,155	4,930

The Katanga line also extends to Port Francqui and thus provides 3 ft. 6 in. gauge track continuously for 3,285 miles from Cape Town into the heart of the Congo Basin. The Portuguese are extending the line from Moçamedes, in Angola, towards Livingstone: this 2 ft. gauge line is being converted to 3 ft. 6 in. but, like other African lines, has gradient problems for in the 80 miles from Assunção to Sa. da Bandeira it rises from 1,600 ft. to 5,700 ft. with an intervening summit of 6,200 ft.

Nyasaland has a natural outlet by the Shire and Zambesi rivers but with the fall, after 1912, in the level of water, due to climatic changes, the railway from Blantyre to Port Herald was extended, using the Ziu Ziu gap, to Chindio on the Zambesi. From here traffic was ferried to Murrasa but at low water the many sandbanks meant the two miles width took up to ten hours' transit. To avoid this delay the Lower Zambesi Bridge, 2¼ miles long, was constructed on deep foundations set in shifting sand. When this bridge was opened in 1934 the Nyasaland line was connected with the Beira and Rhodesian systems. The selected site for the bridge allowed the abandonment of 24 miles of line, which were washed out at every river flood, between Bawe and Chindio.

East Africa

The lines from Mombasa and Dar-es-Salaam represent the rivalry of two colonial powers and the difficult Kenya–Uganda route would never have been selected if the territory had been then under one suzerainty. If the altitudes of the Mombasa–Kampala line be compared with the Euston–Wick line, an indication for British readers is given of the severity of operating because each route has three main summits at about the same distance from the main terminus.

Ca. 250 miles		Ca. 350 miles		Ca. 525 miles	
Shap	914 ft.	Beattock	1,014 ft.	Drumauchdar	1,485 ft.
Nairobi	5,453 ft.	Uplands	7,390 ft.	Timboroa	9,136 ft.

Particular problems are the steep slopes of the rift and the presence of swamps: for example, on the line now nearing completion beyond Kampala to Kasese, near the Congo border, there is a drop of 1,000 ft. in twelve miles and a four-mile-long embankment, 16 ft. high and taking 18 million cubic ft. of earth, is required across Lake George Swamp. Like the South African Railways the lines in East Africa were laid to pioneer standards and sections of the routes have been re-aligned to provide easier working with increasing loads. In 1954 it was agreed to re-align between Tanga and Korogwe in order to eliminate the difficult Bwembwela Bank. The Uganda Railway, as it was first named, was in the construction days notorious for the man-eating lions which ranged among the labour force: in 1900 the Engineer offered £100 reward for the destruction of these pests at Kimaa.

In 1954 a line was opened from the port of Mtwara to serve a ground-nut scheme. Consideration has also been given to schemes for a diagonal line from the Central Tanganyika Railway to join the Rhodesia Railways near Broken Hill and to throw off branches to the south, to join the Mtwara line and towards Lake Nyasa, and to the north to the southern end of Lake Tanganyika. The cost would be immense as apart from the mileage, about 1,400 miles, the terrain is difficult and the economic value doubtful.

Congo

In 1884 it took twenty days and cost £50 a ton to by-pass the Congo Falls between Stanley Pool (Leopoldville) and Matadi. Railway construction was started in 1890 and it was unfortunate that the most difficult works came within the first ten miles: 722 ft. had to be surmounted in $3\frac{3}{4}$ miles. Although made on the 2 ft. 6 in. gauge it was an expensive line, both in the death roll of the labour force and in the capital required. Later the gauge was widened to 3 ft. 6 in. and gradients and curves greatly eased. This 227 miles of line is the key to the Congo for, in the words of Stanley, "without a railway to link the upper reaches of the river to the sea, the Congo is not worth a penny", yet in 1950 this line carried only $1\frac{1}{2}$ million tons of freight—less than that of the Benguela Railway. To allow an outlet under French control the Congo-Océan line was constructed 1921–34 from the port of Pointe Noire eastwards to Brazzaville. Again there was heavy engineering—the Bamba tunnel, 5,550 ft., is among the longer tunnels of Africa, while long viaducts were needed in crossing the highlands.

Further upstream a line from Stanleyville to Ponthierville (600 mm. gauge) and one from Kindu to Kabalo (metre gauge) by-pass rapids on the Congo and Lualaba respectively. These lines supplement the river navigation.

West Africa

In West Africa the railways are either British or French in inspiration and represent the desire to reach the interior from trading ports : the Thiès–St. Louis section of the Dakar–Kayes line was constructed to avoid the seasonal unnavigability of the River Senegal. Gauges in West Africa vary from 2 ft. 6 in. in Sierra Leone to metre in French West Africa and 3 ft. 6 in. in the Gold Coast and Nigeria. The plateau edge is not so formidable as it is south of the equator, but even so in Sierra Leone the first 22 miles in from Freetown have such sharp curves and steep grades in crossing the grain of the country that the 1949 Gatford Report suggested that until this section was re-aligned it could not be worked economically. Mineral wealth has been of major significance in rail development only in Nigeria where a 2 ft. 6 in. gauge line has operated in the Bauchi tin area since 1914. Crossing of the Niger and its tributary the Benue has required long bridges : the bridge over the Benue, 2,624 ft. long, presented the greatest problem in Nigerian railway construction.

From Dakar the railway inland was extended to Koulikoro (808 miles from Dakar), and in 1941 to Segou and thus reached the navigable Niger in French territory. Projects exist to extend this route eastwards, without entering British territory, to French Equatorial Africa and to send a long spur northwards across the Sahara to connect with the Algerian and Moroccan systems.

Northern Africa

From the Mediterranean shore lines extend southwards despite the obstacles of desert and, locally, of high fold mountains. From the first African railway, Alexandria to Cairo, an 80-miles-long extension was made to Suez in 1858 and it provided, until it was abandoned with the opening of the Suez Canal in 1869, a link in the communications chain from Europe to the Orient. This line was restored in 1935 to serve the growing summer resort of Suez. Meanwhile the Egyptian railway system, on 4 ft. 8½ in.

gauge, was extended southwards along the fertile ribbon of the Nile alluvial strip and on 2 ft. 5½ in. gauge to Shellal (converted to standard-gauge from Luxor to Assuan in 1926). A network of 2 ft. 6 in. gauge lines was constructed in the Nile delta lands to allow transport of the cotton crop. There is a gap between the Egyptian, Sudanese (3 ft. 6 in.), Eritrean (3 ft. 1⅜ in.) and Abyssinian (metre) lines although road or river links give some contacts.

During the war a modern steel swing bridge across the Suez Canal and connecting lines were laid by the British Army to link the Egyptian and Palestine railways.

The Sudan Railways owe their origin to a military line of 1897–8 but have been extended westwards to tap the gum traffic of El Obeid and eastwards to Port Sudan on the Red Sea. The Ethiopean Railway was constructed by a French company from the port of Djibuti in French Somaliland to Addis Ababa and, owing to the difficult relief, has long banks of 1 in 40. The Eritrean Railway, with a ropeway to Asmara, runs from Massawa, on the Red Sea, to Agordat and has gradients as steep as 1 in 28½.

Along the desert coast from the Nile to Tunisia are lines which run parallel with the coast or for short distances into the desert. In Tunisia is a 4 ft. 8½ in. gauge network from Bizerta and Tunis and the much longer metre-gauge system south of Tunis which serves, *inter alia*, the phosphate workings. The Algerian system is dominated by the standard-gauge axial line which runs from Tunisia to Morocco and from this short spurs run to the coast, and longer spurs southwards. Most of these spurs are of narrow gauge—3 ft. 5⅛ in., metre and 1 ft. 11⅝ in.—and the network is not so effective as it could have been for transport. In Morocco most lines are of standard-gauge and they carry a heavy ore traffic which is the greatest in North Africa. Standard-gauge lines were extended south in 1941 from eastern Morocco to the Colomb–Béchar coal basin which is also served by a narrow-gauge line from Oran in Algeria. During the war, using slave labour working under appalling conditions, an extension was commenced by the Vichy Government southwards to another coal basin. This was part of an old French dream to have a Mediterranean–Niger link but, even under the incentive of German war needs and with but slight structural works, it made little progress.

NORTH AMERICA

Until 1800 the settlers in North America were penned in by the Alleghenies and Appalachians and as the desire to pass beyond became realizable, railways were being evolved in England. But for a series of chances and the industrially undeveloped nature of the economy the United States might have been the birthplace of the first commercially successful lines. The first railway recorded in North America was a short line used in 1795 to carry bricks from kilns on Beacon Hill, Boston, to a street below and the first railway company to construct and operate a line was the Granite Railway carrying stone from Quincy Quarry to Milton, 3 miles: opened in 1826 it did not carry passengers until 1871. George Stephenson, discouraged at home, had considered emigrating to the United States in 1807 and if he had done so the evolution of the locomotive in Northumberland would have lost his inspiration and the first trunk lines the benefit of his shrewdness.

In 1825 William Strickland visited England and studied the possibility of using a combination of railways and canals for the United States. By about 1832 his proposals were implemented for the linkage between Philadelphia and Pittsburg:

Philadelphia Columbia	Railroad transport of half a canal boat, horse-drawn
Columbia–Hollidaysburg	Canal following Susquehanna and Juanita rivers
Hollidaysburg–Johnstown	Portage rails carrying canal boats on inclined planes with rise of 2,007 ft.
Johnstown–Pittsburg	Canal

It was not completely satisfactory because ice closed the service in winter but ten years before it was replaced, in 1852, by the Pennsylvania R.R., it had been described by Charles Dickens.[1]

"On Sunday morning we arrived at the foot of the mountains, which is crossed by railroad. There are ten inclined planes; five *a*scending, and five *de*scending; the carriages are

[1] *American Notes*, 1842. Chapter X.

dragged up the former, and let slowly down the latter, by means of stationary engines; the comparatively level spaces between, being traversed sometimes by horse and sometimes by engine-power, as the case demands. Occasionally the rails are laid upon the extreme verge of a giddy precipice; and looking from the carriage window, the traveller gazes sheer down, without a stone or scrap of fence between, into the mountain depths below."

Meanwhile other pioneer lines had been created. The Delaware and Hudson Canal Co. was founded in 1823 to carry, *inter alia*, anthracite by a gravity- and rope-operated railway from Carbondale to the canal and in 1829 the company tried out the *Stourbridge Lion*, the first locomotive to run in the New World. Later this line provided part of the shortest route from New York to Montreal. The pioneer common-carrier company was that owning the Baltimore and Ohio R.R. which had its first section opened, with horse-power, in 1830 and later tried out the first American-built locomotive, *Tom Thumb*.[1] It was not until 1852 that the Ohio was reached by this railway.

The mileage of railways in North America increased very rapidly: the U.S.A. had 23 miles in 1830, 9,021 in 1850, 30,635 in 1860, 93,296 in 1880 and 264,378 in the peak year of 1915. The Canadian route mileage is not so great and the increase came later (*see* p. 123). Part of the rapid extension was due to the ease of laying surface lines across the prairies and in the U.S.A. the 'eighties saw 74,720 miles opened to traffic. Such a rate was impossible in settled European countries. Undoubtedly there had been over-expansion of facilities: rival lines had been laid, as needlessly as in Britain, and when this was realized the metals of one were frequently lifted, particularly in time of war. Railway abandonments have been formally recorded in the U.S.A. since 1917 and from then until 1948 33,095 route-miles, that is more than half as much again as the route-mileage of British Railways, had been discarded and as in the same period only 11,234 miles had been built this meant a net annual reduction of about 700

---

[1] The Mount Clare Bridge, Baltimore MD., completed in 1829 is claimed to be the oldest railway bridge still in use but this claim cannot, without reservation, be maintained. *Vide* p. 13.

miles. Reasons for the abandonments included duplication of facilities, extensive damage by floods which was not worth restoring and loss of patronage. The peak year for abandonments was 1942 when 2,516 miles was lifted largely to provide materials for war purposes. In Canada there has also been some abandonment but to a lesser extent as the network had not been provided so lavishly.

Whilst the demands of traffic have been for east–west services what might be described as the geographical, or natural, routeways are aligned longitudinally. Occasionally some of the railway systems are north–south, for example, the Illinois Central R.R., but most are directed to suit the dominant direction of traffic and reach to key points in the barriers. The political frontiers cut the landforms in such a manner that the natural routeways are not always followed. The arbitrary Forty-ninth Parallel fortunately allows Vancouver to be reached by the Fraser and Thompson valleys and link with connecting passes over the Canadian Rockies while for the United States the Columbia and its tributaries afford routeways. Many of the southern valleys of the Canadian sector of the cordillera drain southwards and have their northern portions lake-filled which meant that it was easier to provide routes to serve these valleys from United States' territory. When the Crow's Nest branch of the C.P.R. from Lethbridge to Hope was completed in 1930 and given fast, perennial services to the east and to Vancouver, traffic on branches of the G.N.R., which had previously led the traffic to Spokane and Seattle, so declined that most were closed. In the east a logical flow for traffic from the Mohawk valley is to cross at Niagara to the Lake Peninsula and across Michigan to Chicago; this route is followed by a number of express trains.

Virtually all the North American mileage is of standard-gauge and there are 48 points on the U.S.A.–Canada frontier and 11 on the U.S.A.–Mexico where the railway crosses and many services are international.

United States

The railways of the Unites States have been built up into systems much as occurred in Britain: local lines absorbing connections and thus providing trunk routes. Sometimes there was

H

violent opposition to these amalgamations of interest and one notorious case of 1853 was the uprising at Erie, Pennsylvania, when, to avoid the need for passengers to change trains between Buffalo and Cleveland, it was decided that the 6 ft. gauge from the east should be narrowed to match the 4 ft. 10 in. of the line to the west and no longer would passengers be subjected to the expense and inconvenience of travelling a mile by road between the two termini at Erie. Vested interests destroyed for several years all attempts to connect the two lines.

Another example of opposition to unification is that which was experienced for the route between Albany and Buffalo. In these 197 miles passengers had to transfer trains four times, having to buy separate tickets each time ; nevertheless public opinion prevented the amalgamation for three years. Of the early railways in the U.S.A. only two, the Baltimore and Ohio and the Erie, were conceived and planned from the first as main arteries and most were merely to join slightly separated places. Of the first 95 lines constructed 32 were each less than 20 miles long.

Fear of large companies came from abuse of monopoly and unfortunately the financial system of the U.S.A. aided control by a minority which dominated a holding company. Railways could obtain mortgages and quickly be bankrupted. The story of the financial history of the Western Pacific R.R. Co. serves to illustrate the vicissitudes through which an American railroad could quickly pass : 1903 incorporated as the Western Pacific Railway, 1911 line completed but cost bankrupted the company, 1916 reincorporated Western Pacific R.R. Co., 1935 again went bankrupt, 1944 reorganization with new capital structure. The sources of capital were varied in an endeavour to get railways quickly : the legislature of Illinois, when the population numbered only $\frac{4}{5}$ million, sanctioned the construction of over 1,300 miles of line, in addition to roads and canals, at a cost of over $10 million. By Land Grants, municipal and county bonds capital was obtained. With weak financial safeguards the communities frequently experienced disaster. The State of Ohio made it illegal for a community to issue bonds to aid a railway and the city of Cincinnati, to avoid this control, constructed on its own account the line to Chattanooga and leased it, with satisfactory results, to a company to work.

As Figure 3 indicates, this country, whether in relation to area or population, is not uniformly covered by railways. A simple analysis of the network suggests that it could be considered in three units—the north-east, the south-east and the western—but this is not satisfactory because it includes too great divergencies. The regional division here adopted takes into account the historical traffic flows and fusions of interest, and thus there is an overlap between regions. These regions are those of Professor William Z. Ripley, enunciated in the classic report *Interstate Commerce Commission*: *Consolidation of Railroads, 1921*. Ripley's regions are:

> Trunk Line Territory
> New England Region
> Chesapeake Region
> South-Eastern Region
> Western Transcontinental Region
> South-Western Gulf Region

Trunk Line Territory

From the Atlantic seaboard (New York to Washington) to both the interior cities of Chicago and St. Louis, which owe their origin to water-connections, five main routes extend:

Route	Valleys used	Summit height, ft.	Key town
New York Central	Hudson–Mohawk	920	Batavia[1]
Erie–Wabash	Susquehanna	1,779	Binghampton
Lackawanna–Nickel Plate	Susquehanna	1,739	Binghampton
Pennsylvania	Susquehanna–Juanita	2,192	Harrisburg
Baltimore and Ohio	Potomac–Shenandoah	2,270	Cumberland

Between the Atlantic tidewater and the Interior plains extend the numerous, parallel ridges of the Appalachians and Alleghenies. The routes across are few and difficult and for long the ridges were a barrier in the westward expansion: the story of the

[1] The summit on this route between New York and Chicago is at Kendallville, Indiana, with 995 ft.

influence of these mountains on the communication pattern is fascinatingly told by Professor Albert P. Brigham in *From Trail to Railway through the Appalachians* (Boston, 1907). In his words (p. 85):

". . . first, how the Indian's path was beaten deeper and wider by the hoofs of the pack horse, bearing goods to sell and barter in the wilderness; then how strips of forest were cut down to make room for the Conestoga wagons and the gay stages that swept through from Philadelphia to Pittsburgh. These in their turn became old-fashioned when the canal and Portage Railway were done, and now [1907] we sit in a [Pennsylvania R.R.] car that is like a palace, and think canals and Conestogas very old stories indeed."

The few river gaps focused the railway systems which fan out to the east and the west.

Chicago was a lodestone for the early companies and is now, with 8,000 miles of track in and around the city, one of the world's greatest railway centres. About 1,700 passenger trains and 2,400 freight trains originate or terminate daily in the city. This has all come since the first locomotive ran westwards to Elgin in 1850: the first line in from the east was not open until 1852. As a measure of the nodal quality of this city may be instanced that of the railway companies in the United States no less than 23 have Chicago in their title; a few are local terminal and belt-lines but between them they include in their titles places from New York to the Pacific showing how Chicago is of nation-wide interest. Owing to gauge differences the first through train between Chicago and New York did not run until 1867 and was ferried across the river at Detroit. St. Louis, in early days with the benefit of navigation on the Mississippi, was another magnet for the railways because of its strategic position in relation to the Missouri valley.

New England Region

This is a region which is an economic unit on the periphery of the central commercial territory of the United States and has as its principal asset high-grade labour. The well-being of New England depends upon the provision of cheap, inbound raw materials (coal, cotton, iron and steel) and of foodstuffs and on the efficient transport of manufactures. The intricacy of its trade is matched by the efficient articulation of its railway network, which has a pattern dominated by the radial lines from Boston. Separated as industrial New England is by the Taconic and other mountains lying east of the Hudson–Champlain trench the most used rail gateways in the province are south-westwards to New York, west to Albany, and, to a lesser degree, across the northern frontier into Canada. The gateway to Albany was only effectively opened after the construction, with the aid of public funds, of the Hoosac tunnel through the Taconic Mountains.

Chesapeake Region

The Chesapeake and Ohio (as it existed before 1947), the Norfolk and Western and the Virginian Railways provide a network of lines which fan south-eastwards from Kenova and have intricate branches into the soft coal-mining areas of West Virginia and its borders. Coal is moved in great quantities, the companies are little interested in passenger or general freight services, to the Tide Water, to the Great Lakes and to inland centres such as Louisville. The smokeless coal from the New River and Pocahontas fields is moved to Hampton Roads. With its great dependence on the coal traffic the Norfolk and Western Railway Company was in 1953 the only large railway in the U.S.A. to remain entirely faithful to the steam locomotive. On some sections of this line trains are composed of 175 hopper trucks and have a trailing weight, when loaded, of 14,500 short-tons. The severe grades crossing the Alleghanies in the 80 miles between Hinton, W.Va. and Clifton Forge, Va., need special banking locomotives although the train load is less than that hauled on easier sections such as that from Columbus to Toledo.

South-Eastern Region

This region, south of the Ohio and Potomac rivers and east of the Mississippi, contrasts sharply with the regions to the north and west. This south-eastern area is dominated by seasonal traffic —crops and passengers—although industrial developments, such as that at Birmingham, Alabama, and phosphate-rock workings at Florida, are tending to give a more uniform traffic.

The southern states were not laggard in the introduction of railways : for example, Virginia had in 1840 360 miles. The states of Georgia, Alabama and Mississippi were handicapped in providing railways until the Indian nations had departed into the west. By chance the southern railways were at first dominated by the 5 ft. gauge and this emphasized their diversity of interest from the northern states which came to a head in the Civil War. During the military operations railways played some part, for example the line between Louisville and Nashville had the track and bridges wrecked and relaid three or four times in the campaigns which flowed and ebbed across Kentucky and Tennessee. As material had to be drawn from the northern states the final rebuilding was on standard-gauge. The first all-rail connection with these southern states and New York was not completed until 1887.

The ridges and valleys of the old fold mountains continue into this region and the routeways are affected by the through valleys. One of the most useful of these gaps is the Cumberland which was used by Boone's Trail (Wilderness Road) and gives access to Kentucky: it is now followed by the Louisville and Nashville R.R. The map of any of these trans-Appalachian railways shows the north-east to south-west alignment which is adopted as the engineers follow the valleys connecting the various gaps.

Western Transcontinental Region

The strategic pattern of the western routes depends partly on the crossing of the Mississippi river system and partly on the passes which cross the more difficult sections of the western cordillera, which lie to the east and west of the intermontane plateaux. The most rigorous mountains to cross are from Spokane (Wash.) to Pueblo (Colo.) and then south-westwards to Albuquerque (New Mex.). The routes of the U.S.A. lie in three groups (the Canadian added for comparison).

There were no railways west of the Mississippi in 1847 and it was not until a decade had passed that a traveller could approach this river behind a steam locomotive. Citizens of Cincinnati and St. Louis were worried by the growing dominance of Chicago and encouraged the construction of a line to join the two places. This was the first effective attack on the monopoly of the Mississippi

	Route	Miles	Summit ft.
Canadian:			
Canadian National Railway	Winnipeg–Yellowhead Pass–Prince Rupert	1,745	3,719
Canadian National Railway	Winnipeg–Yellowhead Pass–Vancouver ..	1,567	3,719
Canadian Pacific Railway	Winnipeg–Rogers Pass–Vancouver ..	1,473	5,332
Northern:			
Great Northern Railway	St. Paul–Spokane–Seattle	1,836	5,213
Northern Pacific Railway	St. Paul–Butte–Spokane–Seattle ..	1,904	5,596
Chicago, Milwaukee, St. Paul and Pacific R.R.	St. Paul–Aberdeen–Spokane–Seattle	1,778	6,347
Central:			
Union Pacific R.R.	Omaha–Sherman–Pocatello–Portland	1,784	8,013
Denver and Rio Grande Western R.R. and Western Pacific R.R.	Denver–Glenwood–Salt Lake City–San Francisco	1,535	9,192
Central Pacific (now Southern Pacific) ..	Salt Lake City–Reno–San Francisco	786	*7,017
Southern:			
Atchison, Topeka and Santa Fe R.R.	Kansas City–Flagstaff–San Diego ..	1,902	7,622
Southern Pacific Lines	New Orleans–El Paso–Yuma–Los Angeles ..	2,273	4,739

* This was the height before the new tunnel was bored which gives a summit of 6,886ft. for eastbound traffic.

steamboats since they had been introduced in 1829. In the 'forties about two million square miles were occupied as a result of the overland hegiras which swept over America and the demand for improved facilities was nationwide.

Political jealousies delayed for twelve years the building of the first railway to the Pacific and the route was not determined until after a survey the results of which were published in eleven elaborate volumes reporting upon the geography, Indian life and natural history of the West. President Lincoln signed in 1862 the Bill authorizing commencement but construction did not start until 1864 : this delay was partly due to the Civil War and partly to a quarrel over the gauge. The decision to construct to 4 ft. $8\frac{1}{2}$ in. meant that other railway companies, if they wished to participate in the transcontinental traffic, converted their track to allow through running.

As the railways from the east approach the Mississippi so they focus on the bridging points and the number of lines continuing westwards is reduced ; the same occurs as the railways approach the passes across the cordillera. The so-called *granger* lines[1] serve the plains and basically rely upon local traffic whereas the transcontinental routes depend upon through traffic. This difference can be supported from the following mileages :

	Route Mileage	Average haulage per ton o freight and minerals	Average journey per passenger (non-season)
Chicago and N.W. system	9,443	$227\frac{1}{2}$	$135\frac{3}{4}$
Union Pacific system ...	9,821	611	734

[1] In the early 1870s, when wheat provided the main cash crop, and almost the only commodity originating in the prairie states of the upper basin of the Mississippi, legislation was passed forcing the companies to charge for all grain handled at the lowest rates ever quoted. This legislation was a result of the activities of a farmers' fraternal association known as The Grange, hence it was called the Granger movement and the companies affected became known on Wall Street as the Granger Lines. The legislation was extremely ill-inspired because companies could not afford to pay interest on loans and new companies would not invest within the states affected so by 1876 these laws were either repealed or had become a dead-letter.

COMPLETION DATES OF TRANSCONTINENTAL RAIL ROUTES

Company	Route	Year
Union Pacific and Central Pacific (now Southern Pacific)	Omaha to Sacramento	1869
Atchison, Topeka and Santa Fe and Southern Pacific	Kansas City to southern California	1881
Southern Pacific	New Orleans to southern California	1883
Northern Pacific	Yellowstone River valley	1883
Canadian Pacific	Vancouver	1885
Oregon Short Line and Oregon Railway	Pacific north-west	1885
Atchison, Topeka and Santa Fe	Chicago to California	1888
Great Northern	Great Lakes to Everett (Wash.)	1893
San Pedro, Los Angeles and Salt Lake Railway (now Union Pacific)	Salt Lake City to southern California	1905
Chicago, Milwaukee and St. Paul R.R. (now C., M., St. P. and Pacific R.R.)	Chicago to Seattle	1909
Spokane, Portland and Seattle	Spokane to Seattle	1910
Western Pacific	Salt Lake City to San Francisco	1910
Grand Trunk Pacific (now Canadian National)	Prince Rupert	1914
Canadian Northern (now Canadian National)	Vancouver	1915

The best of the transcontinental routes is that of the Union Pacific, historically the first and choosing the central route from Omaha and Kansas City, and able, in conjunction with other lines, such as the Southern Pacific (which incorporated the former Central Pacific), to cover the whole western seaboard from Portland to Los Angeles. Construction of this centrally placed line was aided by liberal land grants (*see* p. 29), and the work was done rapidly and there has had to be heavy reconstruction. As recently as 1953 a major improvement was the avoidance of Sherman Hill (between Dale Creek and Cheyenne) and the provision, at the cost of moving seven million cu. yds. of earthworks, of easier grades and easy curves for westbound traffic. The Union Pacific is unique among the transcontinental systems in having refrained from entrance to Chicago over its own metals and traffic is delivered to seven systems but the dominating link is the well-constructed double-track line of the Chicago and North Western Railway.

Except in the Pacific states there is not a great demand for north–south links within the mountain area. In 1932 a new line was opened from Klamath Falls (Ore.) to Keddie (Cal.) and it had to surmount a rise of 2,520 ft. within 38 miles. The works on this line are substantial: there are high viaducts, ten tunnels and, in the Wolf Creek Canyon, the Hollenbeck horseshoe curve which, only 2,700 ft. long, has a curvature of two-thirds of a circle.

The United States owes much to its transcontinental lines and even today the services knit the economy in a manner which could not be done by any other transport agency. To take but one item as an example, fruit and vegetables are transported in train loads across the continent to feed the vast urban markets. Without these routes, the oldest of which has been open only for three generations, the United States might well have fragmented into smaller political units.

South-Western Gulf Region

The great territory which lies south of the main line from El Paso to Kansas City, south of the Missouri and west of the Mississippi is divided by the Ozark-Ouachita upland which appears within the network as a negative area with few lines. In this territory there was an optimistic over-provision of lines followed by frequent bankruptcies and abandonments. Lines cross this region from the industrial north to the ports of the Gulf coast and to the Mexican frontier. The principal points of contact with Mexico are Brownsville (near the mouth of the Rio Grande), Laredo, Presidio and El Paso.

Canada

The two principal railway-operating concerns in Canada are the State-owned Canadian National and the company-owned Canadian Pacific, but there are 34 other concerns including the 574 miles long Temiskaming and Northern Ontario owned by the Province of Ontario. Some systems of the United States also extend into Canada : the New York Central (489 miles), Chesapeake and Ohio (319 miles), Wabash (245 miles), Great Northern (223 miles) and Northern Pacific (74 miles) are those with an appreciable mileage.

Canada, with immense distances and a population less than one-third of that of Great Britain, has the further problem of its settled areas being separated by wide expanses of wilderness. As with south of the border the interior lowlands could not be settled until railways were provided which could handle the movement of the cash crop. The first line in Canada was from Quebec to La Prairie, 16 miles long, opened in 1836 and worked from 1837 by a steam locomotive.

The second line was from Montreal to Lachine in 1847 and the third to St. Hyacinthe in 1848 but by 1850 there were still only 66 miles of route, and these were solely of local significance. The railway era for Canada commenced in 1851 with the passing of an Act authorizing the line to connect Lower and Upper Canada and thereafter the mileage increased rapidly—1860 2,065 miles, 1884 10,273 miles, 1900 17,657 miles, 1924 40,061 miles and 1954 42,953 miles. This rapid growth was the result of turning to trunk line construction : for example, the Intercolonial to connect the Maritime Provinces and Lower Canada and the first transcontinental line were completed in 1885, and the second and third transcontinental lines in this century. Across the Prairies Provinces the lines could be laid rapidly. In 1931 the new Hudson Bay route from Manitoba to Churchill was opened.

Canada has been described as a country with too great a

railway mileage and this is partly a result of a cessation of immigration during World War I. It was during this period that companies which had built lines ahead of settlement could not earn sufficient revenue to pay interest on their bonds so, following the Drayton-Acworth Report, the Grand Trunk, Grand Trunk Pacific and Canadian Northern companies were nationalized. Across the prairies lines were too frequently laid parallel and a few miles apart by the C.P.R. and C.N.R. and they became fiercely competitive for there was inadequate traffic to support both. It was an unwise system which absorbed capital and manpower which the Dominion could ill afford.

The White Pass and Yukon line runs from the port of Skagway (Alaska) to Whitehorse (Yukon Territory) and, 110 miles long, this 3 ft. gauge line works in conjunction with navigation on the Yukon river. The first 20 miles demanded heavy engineering for the line rises 2,885 ft. and crosses the trail of the 'ninety-eight goldrush. This isolated line, after being moribund, has acquired a certain strategic importance. The other lines of Canada will be considered in a regional grouping from east to west.

Newfoundland and Labrador

With a population of only just over a third of a million and yet an area larger than Ireland the 705 miles of 3 ft. 6 in. gauge track, now owned by the C.N.R., are of considerable economic value in the rolling terrain. From St. John's to Port-aux-Basques, 547 miles, regular trains connect with steamships to Sydney in Nova Scotia. In late winter snowdrifts cause difficulty, particularly at Topsails (1,800 ft.), and ice accumulating in Cabot Strait hinders the sea passage even with icebreakers. Traffic resources include cod-fishing (May to December) and, when the normal shipping ports are closed by ice, paper from Grand Falls and Corner Brook. This railway system plays no part in international communications but in 1882 it was hoped that the railway would be part, in conjunction with a steamship service to Galway, of the fastest route between London and New York. This site value did not operate until trans-Atlantic aircraft used Gander Airport.

Labrador lacked railways until the Quebec, North Shore and Labrador Railway was recently opened. This line, 320 miles long from Knob Lake to Seven Islands, has a ruling grade of only 1 in

250 against loaded trains and along it is carried iron ore in trains with a trailing load of 14,000 short-tons.

Eastern Canada

Between the Atlantic seaboard and the Great Lakes defined relief features control the route pattern. From ports such as Halifax the rail linkage to the interior is forced to traverse the neck of land separating the Bay of Fundy from Northumberland Strait and then the routes divide : two proceed to Quebec, neither directly, because of the Notre Dame Mountains, nor completely coastwise, because of the ruggedness of the Gaspé Peninsula. A third line manages to pass more directly to Montreal. The St. Lawrence upstream of Quebec is followed by rail routes but there are few bridging points. Quebec Bridge is the lowest bridging point and the construction of this most spectacular cantilever design was marred in 1907 by the collapse of an anchor pier and in the fall 75 men were killed.

Montreal is a key point in the network with lines converging on this bridging point from both sides of the St. Lawrence, both upstream and downstream, from the Champlain gap carrying the services with New York and from the Ottawa valley carrying the more direct routes with the middle west. Montreal is one of the great natural traffic nodes of North America.

The southern edge of the Canadian Shield area lies close to the St. Lawrence and until lines were forced on to it, in the desire to pass north of Lake Superior, it was avoided by the railway engineer. The terrain, with outcrops of resistant rock and intervening muskeg, is not easy to cross. One line was planned to enter the Clay Belt district and during construction valuable mineral lodes were discovered and these have been of considerable benefit as a source of traffic.

Prairie Provinces

West of the Great Lakes and west of the outcrop of the Canadian Shield extends the fertile land of the former prairies and this is now threaded by many lines which have a south-east to north-west grain wherever it is not too arid or too cold for wheat production. When the Northern Pacific line, south of the border, was being constructed it was believed that the winters were so severe that the country was untenable and after the grain-harvest all locomotives, rolling stock and men were withdrawn for five months; this attitude was revised when in the winter 1876–7 the U.S. Government, using Bismarck as a base, conducted a campaign against the Sioux Indians for it was then found that the line could be kept open despite the blizzards. This meant that by the time the lines were being planned across the Canadian prairies the northern winter was not so feared. Winnipeg forms a node for the railway systems with only a hundred miles between the south of Lake Winnipeg and the border. To the east routes extend to lake ports and north of Lake Superior, to the south down the Red river valley into the United States and west and northwest across the prairie lands.

Cordilleran territory

From the foothills the railways are greatly reduced in number owing to the limited number of passes and to the limited amount of traffic. The original C.P.R. route across the mountains was by Kicking Horse Pass which was chosen in preference to a route further south regarded by the Government as too vulnerable to the frontier. The line to Prince Rupert is further from Winnipeg to salt water but uses Yellowhead Pass with a summit of only 3,717 ft.

The Pacific Great Eastern Railway was built, with financial aid from the Province of British Columbia, to join Vancouver to Prince George on the Canadian National line from Edmonton to Prince Rupert. By 1921 it was open from Squamish to Quesnel but by then the C.N.R. had acquired access to Vancouver *via* Kamloops and, traffic not developing on this longitudinal line as had been expected, it was taken over by the Provincial Government. Extensions are being made, with extremely difficult grading works, to Vancouver and northwards to Dawson Creek and Fort St. John which will open up fresh timber and wheat lands.

LATIN AMERICA

Extending from north of 32°N to south of 52°S the mainland portion of Latin America reveals wide differences in the adoption of railways. Some of these differences may be attributed to relief, some to climate and some to the human element. Part of the railway system has been provided to open up the resources of a territory while others are links in major routeways where the district crossed is a barrier, whether of land between two oceans or of barren mountains between two populated lowlands, and is on that account a necessary construction.

Latin America was in general a land where railway construction began late and only as foreign capital became available from Britain, France or the United States. Gauges vary within a country; in Colombia there are three gauges with only six inches difference and in Venezuela five gauges, but there are many isolated sections and, with lack of inter-regional trade, break of gauge has not been the acute problem it has been in Australia except in Argentina and, to a lesser extent, in Mexico. There are some 81,500 miles of railway in Latin America, of which nearly one-seventh is in Mexico, with an absurd variety of gauges with 5 ft. 6 in., 5 ft. 3 in., 5 ft., 4 ft. 8½ in., 3 ft. 6 in., metre, 3 ft., 2 ft. 6 in., 2 ft. 5½ in., and 2 ft.: of these the greatest mileages are with metre, 4 ft. 8½ in. and 5 ft. 6 in.

Along the western seaboard of South America stretch the lofty Andes. These ranges occasionally broaden with intermontane plateaux, while at the northern extremity finger into ranges which enclose the northward flowing Magdalena. Summit heights are lower in Panama but through the states of Central America runs, with decreasing height northwards, a cordillera. In Panama, Nicaragua and in the Isthmus of Tehuantepec are lower passes than occur elsewhere in the whole cordillera of the Americas.

Many of the Latin American countries have closer ties with Europe and the U.S.A. than with one another and part of this may be explained by an inadequate rail network. As Platt so well expressed it: "In transportation, Latin America is like a group of islands. Its separate districts back of ports are isolated from each other and from the outside world except by sea."[1] Geographical factors coupled with political instability have retarded the provision of a network and have resulted in the hinterlands of so

[1] R. S. Platt, *Development and problems of land transport in Latin America*, Proc. Eighth Amer. Sci. Congress, p. 134.

many ports being so limited. Only in rare cases, such as the hinterland behind Buenos Aires, where the rail reticule is adequate, has the port expanded and become a life force in the nation.

Mexico

Railway construction began with the opening of the route *via* Orizaba from Veracruz to Mexico City in 1873. The 'eighties were a period of intensive construction which provided 6,000 miles of line stretching from the capital to Texas and opening a route between the two oceans. It was not easy to build railways in Mexico because, in addition to the central plateau, about 6,000 ft. high, there are steep flanking ridges close to the sea. This period of expansion, inspired by engineers and capital from the U.S.A., was succeeded by a period of political unrest and the railways deteriorated until they were nationalized in 1937. During the Second World War railway traffic increased, particularly on the Laredo–Mexico City–Guatemala route, and technical staff were sent from the U.S.A. to renovate these 1,800 miles. Rolling stock was leased, at one time 8,000 U.S. freight cars were in Mexico, and new lines were constructed to the east of the Gulf of California. A vital rail bridge was constructed during the war over the Suchiate river and, connecting the Mexican Railways with the 3 ft. gauge lines of Guatemala, allowed traffic to flow by rail and so economized shipping space.

Central America

While there are lines serving areas of the states which control this narrow bridge of land, interest concentrates upon the provision of trans-isthmus routes. Before the Panama Canal was constructed there had been other schemes to cross the land. One early project was for a "ship railway" with six lines of rail to carry ships across the Isthmus of Tehuantepec: curves were not feasible and change of direction was to be by turntables. The Tehuantepec Railway was opened from the Atlantic to the Pacific in 1894 but it was of normal standards. Another scheme was to cross Nicaragua and a third was by Panama. Inspired by the Californian gold-rush the Panama R.R. of 5 ft. gauge was opened in 1855. Control of it was acquired by Cornelius Vanderbilt, then by the De Lesseps Canal Company but is now owned by the United States Government. Disease nearly defeated the engineers : Hindu and Chinese coolies, Irish, French, English, Germans, Austrians, Jamaicans and men from the States came and died in great numbers before the line was opened. Before 1855 it took up to five days to cross this treacherous region but, after the opening of the line, only four hours. The saving of time and money was so great, compared with the overland or Cape Horn journeys, that the company could charge heavily for the transit of these 47¾ miles and each passenger paid $25 a trip : for a number of years the company paid a dividend of 12 per cent. It was a popular route for mails and bullion ; in the first five years of operation it carried over 300 million dollars of specie, but lost much of its significance with the opening of the canal and in 1955 it was announced that the railway was to be closed. There is also an inter-ocean line in Costa Rica from Limón to Puntarenos ; from the capital, San José to the Pacific it is electrically operated.

RAILWAY ROUTES ACROSS CENTRAL AMERICA

	Miles
Panama : Cristobal to Panama	47
Costa Rica : Limón to Puntarenos	184
Guatemala–El Salvador :	
Puerto Barrios to Cutuco	425
Guatemala : Puerto Barrios to San José	273
Guatemala : Puerto Barrios to Champerico	353
Mexico : Coatzacoolcos (Puerto Mexicos) to Salina Cruz	
[shortest of trans-Mexican routes]	190

Some of the states have had a network of narrow-gauge lines provided by the United Fruit Company of Boston or the Standard Fruit Company of New Orleans particularly for the banana plantations because the fruit requires immediate shipment. Railway construction is difficult away from the valleys and the Honduran capital, Tegucigalpa, has the distinction of being one of the few inland capitals without a railway—the nearest railhead is at Potrerillos, 246 miles away. While construction is difficult in Central America because of the steep slopes so is maintenance because the torrential rains, acting on these slopes, lead to frequent "wash-outs" of the track.

Andean States

From Colombia to Chile attempts have been made to penetrate into the Andes. From the seashore to the foothills is but a
short distance and so the ascent becomes a problem. Unfortunately there are no low passes. The lowest pass in the 3,000 miles
between Colombia and the south of Chile is not followed by a
railway because there has been no traffic incentive to link
Amazonia with the Pacific seaboard.

In the north the Magdalena valley offers an easier approach
into the Andes but this partially navigable stream is not paralleled
by a line although rails have been laid down to by-pass the rapids :
there will be a through line when the extension northwards from
La Dorada is completed. At present freight from Barranquilla is
carried by river boat for 400 miles, then trans-shipped to rail or
road for the 8,000 ft. climb to Bogotá. Along the Ecuadorian coast
the fronting lowland is relatively wide but although Ecuador has
four lines running in from the coast and has its capital joined to
the principal port of Guayaquil there is little traffic. The Guayaquil
to Quito line has in the mountain section gradients as steep as 1
in 18.

The Peruvian railways consist of lines running in from the
ports, some to serve sugar plantations, and nowhere is there a
network. The longest section is that from Mollendo inland, to
connect with Cusco and navigation on Lake Titicaca, but it does
not carry so much traffic as does the line from Lima to Oroya.
Despite the steep relief there is only one tunnel on the southern
line which is important for the Bolivian wool and alpaca traffic
which it carries. The line from Callao and Lima, using the Rimac
valley, to Oroya was an epic of railway construction and required
elaborate engineering with 67 tunnels, 62 bridges and 11 zig-zags
and almost continuous curving to make the ascent to the Galera
tunnel summit at 12,873 ft. The bulk of the climb is concentrated
in 73 miles and although sections are at 1 in 22, the traffic is
worked solely by adhesion. On the zig-zags the train is always
pulled by the locomotive, with delays for switching at each angle,
because of the liability to landslides making pushing dangerous.
Snowfall is so slight that it is not an obstruction but during the
rainy season landslides are a menace to the safety of the works
(*see* p. 41). Traffic on this Peruvian Central line is considerable

for it supplies and is fed by the produce of the rich Montana mineral district with its great coppermines of Cerro de Pasco.

Landlocked Bolivia is dependent on railways for the movement of most commodities and is now joined directly by rails, which connect at Oruro, to Arica and Antofagasta on the Pacific and indirectly *via* Lake Titicaca to Mollendo while to the Atlantic are connections with ports of the Argentine and Brazil. The connection from Buenos Aires was only completed in 1925 and the route is difficult near the Argentine frontier; from Leon to Volcan is 9 miles of rack operation which takes $1\frac{3}{4}$ hours to surmount. Works are in progress to connect the eastern and western parts of Bolivia and when completed will provide a 2,365 miles long transcontinental linkage between Arica on the Pacific and Santos on the Atlantic seaboard. The Brazilian Government have given financial support to this metre-gauge project. One of the handicaps to railway operation on the high plateau is the rarefied air and when diesels were introduced on the line joining La Paz to Guaqui, on the shores of Lake Titicaca, it was found necessary to supercharge, otherwise the power was lost, and to increase the size of the brake compressors.

Southwards from Peru extends the ribbon of Chile where railway construction has been more liberal than in any other Andean state. In the narrow valley between the coastal ranges and the foothills of the Andes there extends from Puerto Montt in the south to La Calera, near Santiago, a 5 ft. 6 in. gauge longitudinal line which is extended northwards by metre-gauge track to Iquique. From this spinal route branches on various gauges run west to the coast and east into the Andean foothills. Many of these branches, provided to serve nitrate plant and metalliferous mines, were made with capital from Britain or the U.S.A. The longitudinal line, although paralleled by an effective coastwise navigation, was considered essential for national unity.

The nitrate area is opened by spurs so that fuel oil can be carried to the concentrating centres (*oficinas*) and the concentrates exported. The 3 ft. 6 in. gauge Taltal line can serve as an example of these nitrate railways. It extends for 156 miles inland from the port of Taltal and has branches radiating out from the ganglion point of Ovalo with one extending further to tap a metalliferous district. The nitrate deposits are about 3,000 ft.

above sea-level and, separated from the ocean by coastal ranges, the railways could only be made with steep gradients—there is a rise of 1 in 24 outside Taltal—and most of the lines could not be worked if it were not that most of the load is with the grade. On the Taltal line three-fifths of the traffic is provided by nitrate shipments.

Provision of rail routes to serve the metalliferous centres has been more arduous because they lie within the high land: the branch to serve the coppermines at Collahuasi reaches to 15,835 ft. above sea-level, the highest rail summit in the world. As an example of the dependence of these mines on railways may be instanced the 2 ft. 6 in. gauge Braden R.R. owned by the Braden Copper Company of New York. This line runs from Sewell, with a branch from the Caletones Smelter, to Rancagua and there connects with the broad-gauge longitudinal line and spur to the port of San Antonio. The trains laboriously wind their way along a canyon with curves as sharp as 99 ft. radius and grades as steep as 1 in 21 and bring to the works fuel oil from California and Peru, flotation oil from Scotland, timber from Puget Sound and southern Chile as well as general supplies and daily carry down 300 tons of copper ingots. Originally worked by steam locomotives it is now operated by diesel-electric units.

The Transandine Railway crosses the Andes and is a link in the communication chain between Valparaiso and Buenos Aires. The ascent is made from the west in 50 miles whereas on the east double that distance is used. In the 45 miles from Los Andes is a metre-gauge line which has adhesion working on gradients of 1 in 40 but where these could not be provided is a rack section at 1 in 12½. The metre-gauge continues across the frontier to Mendoza. The total journey of 888 miles from ocean to ocean by this rail route, which uses the Uspallata Pass, requires about 36 hours. When the line was opened throughout in 1910 it was made possible to travel from Hamburg to Valparaiso in less than 20 days: Hamburg to Genoa by rail 2 days, Genoa to Buenos Aires by mail steamer 16 days and thence by rail to Valparaiso 1½ days, and this compared with a sea journey between Buenos Aires and Valparaiso, *via* Magellan Straits, of about a fortnight. The line was closed from 1934–44 by the rupture of a glacier dam which released a flood of water and destroyed stretches of the line on the

Argentine side. There is a plan to lower the present summit of 10,466 ft. by boring a thirteen miles long tunnel under the pass. While this is the most direct route across the Andes it is also possible to make a detour north through Bolivia, using the British-owned Antofagasta line, to the Pacific or to make a detour to the south. From Buenos Aires express trains run *via* Bahia Blanca to San Carlos de Banloche (1,082 miles) and then by lake motor-vessel and 'bus the journey may be made to Puerto Vartas whence there is a diesel service by rail to Puerto Montt and Santiago : this roundabout journey takes 5½ days.

South-Eastern States

This is the only territory of South America where physical conditions do not seriously impede railway construction and operation. Spread across the Pampas, with their maize and wheat traffic, is a network equivalent to the European. From the first line opened in 1857 (6 miles) near Buenos Aires, the system has grown. In 1882 there were only 1,532 miles but in the following ten years it increased to 6,851 miles and this, after the period of stalemate, was followed by other periods of activity particularly from 1904–14. Construction has been continued in recent years ; for example, in 1951 the line was completed to join the coalmines at Rio Turbio in Patagonia with the port of Rio Gallegos, and this 155 miles of 2 ft. 5½ in. line has the distinction of being the most southerly railway in the world. There are now over 25,000 route miles of railway of which 58 per cent were provided by British capital and 11 per cent by French. All the lines are now nationalized.

The dense network of lines in the Pampas thins out rapidly west of the humid "core" and south of Bahia Blanca. Lines extend into the irrigated foothill belt of the Andes and one penetrates directly across the Andes (*see* above) and two into Bolivia.

The railways of Paraguay do not connect with the systems of Argentina or Brazil and this landlocked republic is still dependent upon the river link and most of the railways serve to feed the navigation.

Brazil

Railway engineers have had to meet in Brazil the physical obstacles of the 2,500 ft. high scarp of the Serro do Mar, immediately beyond the coastal marshes, and dense, unhealthy forests. The Brazilian plateau may not be very lofty but it does result in difficult operation : for example, on the Leopoldina line the Cantagallo branch climbs for 50 miles with grades as severe as 1 in 30 and, until articulated locomotives were introduced in 1940, loads had to be very restricted. One of the most important lines in Brazil is the short route between Santos and São Paulo. After expensive re-alignment the gradients still cannot be made less severe than 1 in 40.

Railway construction was late in starting although in 1839 Robert Stephenson reported on a project to connect Santos with the interior. The first line opened was that in 1854 from near Rio de Janeiro to near Petropolis. Vast areas are still devoid of railways for this immense country of $3\frac{1}{4}$ million square miles has only 23,000 miles of line. Most of the lines are found in the north-east and south-east and, as yet, there is no connection between the two regions although it is planned to link them by an inland line joining the railheads of Montes Claros and Ourives. New lines are still being opened : for example, in 1938 an important line from Mayrink towards Santos which demanded large and frequent culverts to cope with the torrential rain which in this district totals 160 in. a year. In 1945 a road-railway bridge, equipped to take both metre and 4 ft. $8\frac{1}{2}$ in. gauge rolling stock, was opened across the River Uruguay and thus links Argentina, Brazil and Uruguay.

Amazonia has no railways of significance although it covers twice the area of the Mississippi basin. During the Brazilian rubber boom the Madeira–Mamoré line was built to circumvent the rapids. An attempt, defeated by fevers, was made in 1878 but effective work did not commence until 1907. Again it looked as if malaria would conquer ; the hospital at Candelaria treated 30,430 patients between 1908–11, but the disease was beaten by quinine. Although this line might function as a link between Bolivia and the outer world traffic on its 227 miles has never been great. Maintenance cannot be kept at a high standard and, with a maximum speed of 16 m.p.h., the weekly train takes two days on the journey.

North-Eastern States

Between Venezuela and the Guianas varied obstacles face the railway engineer—steep fold mountains in the west, the Guiana highlands in the east and between the ill-drained valley of the Orinoco. Of the nine public railways extending in from the ports until recently only two were connected by a link line. The emphasis is on transport by sea and river but the apparently valuable Orinoco, unlike the Magdalena, is a backwater. Because of the lack of local interest in railways most have been constructed by foreign capital. The oldest railway in South America is the Demerara Railway in British Guiana.

West Indies

Railways have been constructed in a number of the West Indian Islands.

Island	Gauge	Mileage	Traffic
Jamaica	4' 8½"	281	Bauxite, fruits and sugar
Trinidad	4' 8½"	120	Sugar, cacao, citrus fruits, petroleum, asphalt
Cuba	4' 8½"	2,522 ⎫	
	3' 0"	81 ⎬ Sugar	
	2' 5½"	50 ⎭	
Santo	3' 6"	103 ⎫	
Domingo	2' 6"	63 ⎬ Lime fruits, cacao	
Haiti	3' 6"	112 ⎫	
	2' 6"	75 ⎬ Sugar	
Puerto Rico	Metre	220	Coffee, sugar, cacao, tobacco

In Cuba there are also over 7,000 miles of track, on seven gauges varying from 4 ft. 8½ in. gauge down to 2 ft. 2 in. gauge devoted to the transport of the canes to the sugar mills while in Santo Domingo (Dominica) plantation railways have about five times the mileage of the public service lines. In Santo Domingo, on the narrow-gauge track, was a bank of four miles at 1 in 20 which was worked by rack rail until it was converted in 1922 to adhesion operation with Shay geared-locomotives. Cuba, with a maximum width of only 55 miles, has well distributed harbours and the axial railway suffers severe competition from the shipping services.

The Jamaica Government Railway was opened from Kingston to Angelo in 1845, as a company line to the design of an Edinburgh engineer. This, the oldest British colonial railway, has had chequered ownership: bought by the Government in 1879, sold to an American syndicate in 1890 and re-acquired by the Government in 1900. The mountainous interior has needed gradients of 1 in 30 and these require freight trains to be double-headed. In addition to the public service lines there are private lines to serve the sugar and banana plantations and the bauxite mines.

AUSTRALASIA

Australia

On account of the varying gauges (see Table, p. 18), the network is not nearly so effective as the map suggests and unfortunately there are no waterways, perennially navigable, to supplement the rail. Railway construction has frequently preceded settlement and, too often, to reduce the financial burden, the works have been executed in a makeshift fashion which has later demanded expensive restoration. Aridity has been a substantial handicap in operation and there are also grading difficulties for, although the highest peak of Australia, Kosciusko, is only 7,318 ft. the fold mountains are close to the south-east coast.

The first Australian line was from Port Melbourne to Flinders Street (2½ miles, 5 ft. 3 in. gauge, opened in 1854), the second from Sydney to Parramatta (14 miles, 4 ft. 8½ in. gauge, opened 1855), and the third from Port Adelaide to Adelaide (7½ miles, 5 ft. 3 in. gauge, opened in 1856[1] and the first State-owned line in the then British Empire). This simple sequence reveals the keynote of so much of the later development—the entry from a port towards the interior and the autonomy of the states over the selection of gauge. To this day the network is still, in broad terms, coastal and whilst the area of the continent is about that of the United States and Alaska the 21,165 miles of railway route have been provided for a population of only 8·4 million, of whom two out of every five live in the capital cities. The mileage at first

[1] In 1854 a horse-drawn railway was opened between Port Elliot and Goolwa, 6 miles.

increased slowly[1] and connection between the various state capitals was not made until:

> 1883 for Melbourne and Sydney
> 1887 for Melbourne and Adelaide
> 1889 for Brisbane and Sydney
> 1917 for Perth and Adelaide

Some of the routes were beyond the resources of the states, and the Commonwealth, after its inception in 1901, had to assist. In 1913, on the threshold of revival of road transport, Western Australia had nearly 17 yards of rail per head of population. Railway construction had out-distanced the then developed resources which depended upon very fluctuating outputs of mining and agricultural and pastoral activities. Until the Commonwealth gave assistance Western Australia could not hope to complete a rail linkage with Adelaide. While the area per mile of line open might be considerable the population density, which produced the traffic on which the lines depended, was slight.

COMPARISON OF 1913 AND 1951 SITUATIONS IN RELATION TO AREA AND POPULATION PER MILE OF LINE OPEN

	Population		Area in Sq. Miles	
	1913	1951	1913	1951
New South Wales ...	457	515	78	48
Victoria	372	504	24	19
Tasmania	287	401	40	36
South Australia	216	187	196	99
Queensland	137	185	145	102
Western Australia ...	105	117	339	197
Northern Territories ...	23	32	3,603	1,030

Now with increased population the situation in some states is not so severe, but even so, when allowance is made for traffic which will travel by road, it is clear that the Australian network is unduly liberal against the population and that the traffic densities, except in favoured areas, can never be great.

[1] In the 1860s construction averaged 78 miles whereas in the 1880s it averaged 594 miles a year.

Distances are very considerable and, with five breaks of gauge, it is possible to travel by rail from Mount Isa (Queensland) for 5,451 miles to Wiluna (W.A.). Inter-capital distances are also appreciable : Brisbane to Sydney 613 miles, Sydney to Melbourne 589 miles, Melbourne to Adelaide 483 miles and Adelaide to Perth 1,622 miles. Unfortunately many of the mileages within the states are also great and across sparsely settled country which produces but little traffic, for example, Mount Isa to Brisbane is 1,435 miles and Wiluna to Perth 709 miles.

In 1846 W. E. Gladstone, then Colonial Secretary, recommended 4 ft. 8½ in. as the standard gauge for the Australian colonies but locally 5 ft. 3 in. was agreed upon. In 1852 a new engineer for the N.S.W. line inland from Sydney reverted to 4 ft. 8½ in. and thus inaugurated the possibility of the pernicious breaks of gauge which have since bedevilled Australian railways.[1] Numerous Committees and Commissions have considered the matter for the burden on transport of cost and time is a major issue : in 1912 trans-shipment cost 2s. 6d. a ton for general merchandise and 3s. 0d. a truck on livestock. No charge was levied on wool but the expenditure was there although concealed. The recommendations of military advisers stressed the value of a uniform gauge and the force of their arguments was realized in the defence of Australia during the Second World War. In addition to delays at break-of-gauge points supply of supplementary locomotive power and rolling stock to meet war needs was greatly complicated by the variety of gauges. Some minor unification has been done ; for example, standard gauge has been provided between Sydney and Brisbane by opening the Kyogle route at a cost of £4 million, but, whilst this new route saved five hours of travelling time between the two capitals, not all of it can be credited to having a uniform gauge. The Report of Sir Harold Clapp in 1944 recommended complete conversion to standard-gauge at a cost of about £200 million (which estimate had risen to £280 million five years later). For some time all 5 ft. 3 in. gauge lines have been made to suit reduction and care is being taken in re-equipment to provide convertible stock. In any case much of the

[1] It is a music-hall jibe that the success of Australian airways is entirely due to Australian railways ; the breaks of gauge have reduced the possibility of providing fast inter-state services.

stock is becoming obsolete: in 1949, for example, two-fifths of the Queensland locomotives were over 30 years old and due for replacement. Nevertheless, the capital cost is formidable and a compromise scheme for a standard-gauge inter-capital connection has been prepared in lieu of complete conversion.

	Miles	
Darwin–Birdum	317	Conversion from 3 ft. 6 in.
Birdum–Djarra	645	New line
Djarra–Townsville and Winton	901	Conversion from 3 ft. 6 in.
Winton–Longreach	110	Mixed gauge
Longreach–Bourke (via Charles-ville)	523	New line
Bourke–Orange–Sydney (and via Melbourne or Broken Hill) to Port Pirie and Kalgoorlie ...		Existing standard-gauge
Kalgoorlie–Perth	401	New line

The Railways Standardization Agreement Bill was passed by the Federal Parliament in 1946 and it covered works in South Australia, Victoria and N.S.W. but was only ratified by the Parliaments of the first two states. This Act also authorized the completion of the north–south line.

From the ports the railways stretched towards the interior and there was some inter-state agreement over the provision of routes: the Riverina district of N.S.W. was, by arrangement with the state of Victoria, opened up for settlement by railway from Melbourne.

The Trans-Australia line was conceived in 1870 by John Forrest after his five months' crossing of this region where the annual precipitation is only 8 in. but the evaporation rate is 108 in. The distance from Port Pirie to Kalgoorlie is 1,108 miles, equal to that from London to Naples, and the relief features were so slight an obstacle (the line had no tunnels or bridges) that the railway was constructed in five years. The worst sectors are 450 miles of the fantastically eroded surface of the Nullabor Plain (*Nullus arborno* tree) and the 50 miles across the Ooldea sandhills, east of the limestone plain. There is one section of 309 miles without a curve. Water supply is a serious problem and tank wagons carry drinking water from Rawlinna to Cook, 300 miles. Rainfall is liable to occur as a torrential downpour and this may lead to washouts while sandhills drifting across the track also cause trouble.

When the line was opened with steam locomotives it saved three days, compared with the sea journey, from Fremantle to Sydney and so justified the construction although there was no traffic originating on the 800 miles between Kalgoorlie and Tarcoola. Eastwards from Tarcoola are red soil plains which were opened to pastoral farming by the railway. Locomotives were changed at Cook. Haulage of coal and water for the locomotives was an expensive item—with only 88,000 passengers and 104,000 tons of paying freight a year this service haulage accounted for two-fifths of the total gross ton-mileage—and the route was well suited for diesel-electric operation. From dieselization in 1952 there was an increase of speed and, with a saving of £$\frac{1}{4}$ million a year on running expenses, the annual deficit was turned into a temporary surplus. The passenger journey-time between Kalgoorlie and Port Pirie was reduced by 20 hours but much of this advantage was lost for freight by the breaks of gauge. Between Sydney and Perth the mileage would justify five days' journey-time for freight but, with three transfers, it becomes fourteen days : a consequence is that more wagons are required, adding to the capital cost of providing the service, and merchants need to carry larger stocks.

In addition to the east–west link there is the start of a north–south line across the interior with the Central Australian Railway north to Alice Springs and the Northern Australian Railway south from Darwin to Birdum. Railheads were originally at Oodnadatta and Pine Creek but since these lines were taken over by the Commonwealth in 1911 they have been extended. On the North Australian line numerous bridges are required and the greatest of these, 700 ft. long, is over the Katherine river. The rivers in this territory can rise very rapidly with the monsoonal rains. Engineering difficulties between the present railheads are not great but there is an acute water shortage ; the few English names along the proposed route are suggestive of the significance of water points—Tennant Creek, Powell Creek, Newcastle Waters and Daly Creek. The lines were relatively cheap to construct but traffic, except in war, has never been great.[1] Before 1939 there were on the Central Australian line two through trains a week and on the North Australian one in each direction although special livestock and supply trains were run spasmodically. In 1943-4 the weekly service from Port Augusta to Alice Springs was 56 trains in each direction and from Darwin to Birdum 147 trains. This revolution in traffic raised the problem of the supply and maintenance of locomotive power and of rolling stock: locomotives had to be taken from the 3 ft. 6 in. gauge lines of Queensland and South Australia whereas to supplement services on the Trans-Australia line standard-gauge stock was obtainable from North America. The Table on p. 142 summarises the effect of war and, on the Trans-Australia line, the later effect of dieselization. Diesels are being introduced on the other Commonwealth lines following these favourable results.

This Table also shows the great increase of work which can be performed by railways with but slight increases of staff; for example, on the Central Australian line a six-fold increase of ton-miles was performed with a doubling of the pre-war staff.

Although the mileage of Australian railways is considerable, in relation to her resources, it is still found necessary to finance fresh construction. With the post-war exploitation of the Leigh Creek coalfield a standard-gauge deviation line is being built by the Commonwealth to Stirling North, on the existing Central Australia line, to allow two million tons of coal to be hauled each year to Port Augusta.

Western Australia

Over the south-west region of Mediterranean-type climate, and consequent agricultural wealth, there extends on either side of the Perth–Albany route an adequate network of lines. The first railways were privately owned and built in about 1871 from Lockville, to open up *karri* forests, and from Rockingham to aid the export of *jarra* timber. The first state line was opened in 1879 from Geraldton to Northampton (33½ miles), when the

[1] It was claimed in 1903 that if this line were built mails and passengers, travelling by the Siberian Railway, could pass from London to Adelaide in 17 days. Circumstances have so changed that this line cannot play a part in such a movement.

AUSTRALIA : COMMONWEALTH RAILWAYS.

[Based on Reports on Commonwealth Railways Operations.]

	Cent. Aust. Rly. 771			N. Aust. Rly. 316			Trans-Aust. Rly. 1,108		
Route-mileage	1938–9	1943–4	1953–4	1938–9	1943–4	1953–4	1938–9	1943–4	1953–4
Train-mileage, million	0·28	1·85	0·9	0·03	0·74	0·07	0·6	0·8	0·9
Ton-miles, million	87·6	595·5	358·5	4·1	134·7	9·5	257·4	465·6	564·5
Revenue, £M†	0·1	1·6	1·5	0·06	0·8	0·07	0·3	1·0	1·8
Expenditure, £M†	0·2	1·0	1·4	0·05	0·5	0·1	0·4	0·9	1·4
Staff employed ..	451	940	*	136	787	*	1,394	1,902	*

* Comparable figures are not obtainable but there are difficulties over man-power owing to the attractions of other highly paid work.

† Australian £.

population of the state was only 25,000, to assist the mining industry. By 1890 there were 505 miles of line (about one eighth of the present mileage), partly privately owned and constructed with the aid of land-grants, which were supported by 96 persons per mile of line open. The discovery of dramatic quantities of gold—Southern Cross (1887), Coolgardie (1892), Kalgoorlie (1893), and, later, the Murchison district—resulted in a rapid extension of railway facilities into the semi-desert regions. Southern Cross was reached in 1894, Kalgoorlie in 1897, Laverton in 1905 and, for the Murchison goldfields, Cue in 1898, Meckatharra and Sandstone in 1910 and Wiluna in 1933. In the six years 1894–9 over a thousand miles of such state-owned lines were built and not until ten years later was attention paid to the provision of light railways to serve the agricultural and pastoral industries. Railway extension to serve the ephemeral mining has been followed by recent removal of track and withdrawing of services from the isolated lines of Hopetown to Ravensthorpe, Port Hedland to Marble Bar and the branch from Mount Magnet to Sandstone. In addition to the 4,108 route-miles of state-owned 3 ft. 6 in. line there are 277 miles of the private Midland Railway and 452 miles of the standard-gauge Trans-Australia line east from Kalgoorlie.

The average capital cost of the lines has been only £5,479 a mile, the lowest in Australia; grades of 1 in 40, and even 1 in 30, and sharp curves are relatively frequent because the engineers lacked the capital for easements. The longest bridge is that of 1,331 ft. over the Swan river near Perth and the only tunnel is the 1,116 ft. bore through the Darling Range, east of Perth. The real problem of operating is not the profile of the routes but for the Eastern Goldfields Railway, in particular, that of water-supply (see p. 72).

Wool and wheat are, by weight, the main items of traffic but coal from Collie, half of which is used on the railway, is taken to all the settled districts of the state. Freightage from shipment of the gold produced is not vital for the well-being of the system but a considerable revenue is obtained from supplying the mines and miners.

South Australia

For a century railways have been operated in this state and the development has been for the shipment of grain and minerals from the three chief ports—Port Adelaide, Port Augusta and Port Pirie. Unfortunately there are considerable lengths of both 5 ft. 3 in. and 3 ft. 6 in. gauge and the standard-gauge of the eastern section of the Trans-Australia line. Port Pirie, since 1937 the meeting point of these three gauges, is a junction unique in Australia.

The most intrictate network is found in the more humid agricultural zone east of Spencer Gulf and lines extend from here east into the lower Murray Mallee region, crossing the Murray by a bridge 1,882 ft. long, north-east to Broken Hill (which sends lead and zinc concentrates to the smelters at Port Pirie), and north to the Central Australia line. To the west of the Spencer Gulf is the Eyre Peninsula which has lines focusing on Port Lincoln. Railway construction found its greatest physical obstacle in the section between Adelaide and Mount Lofty: a tunnel 2,376 ft. long had to be bored and there are gradients of 1 in 45.

In the post-war period substantial strengthening of structure, as well as the virtual elimination of narrow-gauge south of the Port Pirie–Broken Hill line, was achieved and larger wagons and more powerful locomotives were introduced which allowed the traffic to be moved.

Victoria

This state has the greatest mileage of any Australian system in relation to the area and is also supported by the greatest number of people per mile of route. Apart from the mountainous district little of the state is more than eight miles from a railway. The network beyond the complicated highlands known as the Great Dividing Range is dominated by the parallel pattern, with a NNW–SSE alignment, which served to convert the Mallee District into a prosperous farming region. J. W. Gregory summarized the stages of development of the Victorian railways as follows:

		Length (miles)
1854–60	Local lines round Melbourne ...	114
1860s	Melbourne to gold-mining districts ...	276
1870s	Lines to southern agricultural districts ...	1,247
1880s	Lines to north-west plains ...	2,763
1890s	Lines to open up Mallee plains ...	3,238

The mileages are those in the state at the end of each decade. The Dividing Range did not require long tunnels to break a way through : the longest tunnels in the state are near Geelong (1,386 ft.) and in the suburbs of Melbourne (1,357 ft.)

South of the Great Dividing Range the lines are aligned east and west and of these lines the Gippsland, which serves the Yalbourn brown coalfield, is the most important. In 1948–9 the coal traffic was under a million tons but it is now about double that tonnage and to transport it the line was electrified in 1954 using power generated from the brown coal.

New South Wales

The railways of the state cost more per mile than those of the other Australian states because of the parallel ranges and plateaux which lie within 20 to 70 miles of the coast. For decades this upland barrier delayed penetration inland. Even in the Triassic shale area around Sydney the country is undulating and the relief adds to the cost of construction. Every economy possible was made by laying the lines with sharp curves (15 chains radius) and steep gradients (1 in 33). Until 1885 most of the railways were built in the populous agricultural districts, such as the Riverina and New England, but since then extensions have been into the pastoral lands. The line westward from Sydney was originally constructed with zig-zags because with an allowance of only £20,000 a mile tunnelling was impossible. About 1908 5½ miles of deviation line was opened to by-pass the Lithgow Zig-Zag : it cost £350,000 but for most freight trains saved double-heading and for passenger trains half an hour on the journey. The steep relief of N.S.W. has led, as capital became available, to tunnel boring and the aggregate length of the 85 tunnels on the system is 16¾ miles ; the longest tunnel is Woy Woy, 5,871 ft. for double track.

Two of the most important engineering works in Australia are the Hawkesbury and Sydney Bridges. The new Hawkesbury Bridge, opened in 1946, has eight spans (the longest 445 ft.) with a total length of 2,764 ft. The estuary is wider but the gap has been narrowed by embankments because of the difficulty of obtaining in the mud sound pier foundations. Some caissons were sunk 170 ft. below high-water level to provide a firm base. When the original bridge was opened in 1889 it was the longest in the

K

southern hemisphere. The Sydney Harbour Bridge with its main arch of 1,650 ft., four rail tracks and clearance of 170 ft. is one of the great bridges of the world. Many of the minor bridges are of a greater length than would be expected from the normal flow of the rivers and this is because of the heavy rainfall sometimes experienced, 11 in. has been recorded in a day, and the wide spans are to allow the water to escape.

Queensland

This state has the longest of the Australian systems. It focuses on many ports—for example, Brisbane, Rockhampton, Townsville and Cairns—and owing to competition from shipping in waters sheltered by the Barrier Reef the line between Rockhampton and Townsville was not completed until 1923. The lines are more widely spread than other Australian networks, nearly half the mileage is beyond 500 miles from the state capital which compares with $7\frac{1}{2}$ per cent for Western Australia and $2\frac{1}{2}$ per cent for N.S.W., and this leads to administrative and haulage difficulties. There are many "dead-end" routes and these necessitate unproductive running. Parliamentary authority has long been granted for a line Camooweal–Springvale–Windorah–Tobermory which would parallel the east coast and open the interior.

The coastal ranges are lower and further inland than in N.S.W. which means that gradients rarely exceed 1 in 75. From near Rockhampton a rack railway is used to ascend 373 ft. in $1\frac{3}{4}$ miles in order to serve the Mount Morgan gold and copper mines.

Tasmania

The first line in the island was opened in 1871 from Launceston to Deloraine. Unfortunately, with economy in construction in a ravined terrain, the Tasmania lines were designed with unduly sharp curves and steep gradients: on the 2 ft. gauge west coast line, with gradients of 1 in 25 and curves of $1\frac{1}{2}$ chains, loads were limited to 120 tons until the introduction of very powerful locomotives.

The railways were frequently jerry-built, for example with wooden culverts which rotted, with bad alignment and grading and during the inter-war depression the works became decrepit. They were further handicapped by some ancient material including locomotives over fifty years old. The traffic is very vulnerable to road competition, for distances are short between towns, but vigorous efforts are being made to restore the railways. Deviations are planned to eliminate 30 miles of the worst section between Hobart and Launceston. This state railway was the pioneer in Australia in diesel-electric operation of main-line services.

Sources of traffic, apart from agriculture, are cement at Railton, paper-mills at Burnie (fed with pulp timber from the Redpa branch) and at Boyer and the coalmining at St. Mary's. Mining has been the incentive for constructing some of the branch lines, for example, Mount Zeehan silver-lead and Mount Lyell copper.

New Zealand

In 1863 the line from Christchurch to Lyttleton was opened, except for the Lyttleton tunnel ($1\frac{1}{2}$ miles) which was not completed for another four years. By this time the line from Bluff Harbour to Invercargill was open. New Zealand had lines of various broad gauges but in 1870 it was agreed to adopt 3 ft. 6 in. as standard and thereby allow cheaper construction in the mountainous districts. Although some of the lines were built by private enterprise they were later nationalized. There is a limited mileage of mining and timber lines still privately owned. The mileage in 1870 was 46, in 1876 (when the Central Government took over the provincial control) 718, in 1906 2,458, in 1926 3,138 and in 1953 3,530 route-miles of which 130 miles were double track.

New Zealand, with rugged mountains and great rivers, is a very difficult terrain for the railway engineer. The land rises rapidly from the coast and has innumerable deep-cut valleys and wide lower valleys which, in the South Island, may carry rivers swollen by meltwaters. Engineering works are considerable and the capital cost has been enhanced by expensive bridging. Numerous ports provide keen competition for railways in a land where no line can be more than 75 miles from the coast. Railway gradients are an obstacle to fast running, 9 per cent of the total mileage is steeper than 1 in 50, and to keep down the weight of trains meal-halts have replaced since 1917 the heavy dining-car.

Agricultural produce and fertilizers account for over one-third of the freight revenue, minerals for one-fifth and timber for less than one-tenth.

North Island

The system extends to Okaihau which is 618 miles from the railway administration centre of Wellington and in this respect the North Island is comparable with Britain. When the connection between Wellington and Auckland was completed the population of the North Island was not so great as that of Liverpool and Manchester and the financial burden was considerable. The original route *via* Paekakariki had a climb for $4\frac{1}{2}$ miles at 1 in 40 followed by a descent of 1 in 60 for 5 miles to Tawa Flat and over this summit all traffic with Wellington had to be hauled until a deviation line with two long tunnels was provided. The section across the Rimutaka Mountains is at 1 in 13 and worked by the Fell system. This is expensive to operate and leads to many delays so a costly deviation line, with a tunnel nearly $5\frac{1}{2}$ miles long, is being constructed to eliminate this section.

South Island

The east coast line extends from Picton to Invercargill and spurs run into the lower valleys of the Southern Alps; only one of these spurs penetrates to the west coast. This line to Greymouth was expensive to build for, in addition to the Otira tunnel $5\frac{1}{3}$ miles long, there are heavy approach works to Arthur's Pass. A line runs from Nelson to Glenhope, using the Hope river valley, but fails to reach the Westport line and this means that the Greymouth district is relatively isolated from Cook Strait. Construction of the east coast line for long halted with the railhead well south of Picton but the extension from Parnassus, to link with the Picton line, was completed about 1945 and allowed improved connections with a short sea route between the North and South Islands. The east coast line cuts across the rivers draining from the Southern Alps and, because of its numerous bridges, the section in central Otago is known as the Bridge Line.

CHAPTER VII

SERVICES

THE enormous capital sunk in railways and the vast man-power consumed in their construction and operation have the sole purpose of providing transport service, usually commercial but sometimes strategic. Famous named express trains—in Europe the *Blue Train*, the *Rome Express*, the *Simplon-Orient Express*, the *Orient Express*, the *Golden Arrow*, and in America the *Burlington Zephyr*, *El Capitan*, *Denver Zephyr* and *Hiawatha*—all catch the imagination and give a certain glamour to the service. More vital in daily life is the little-advertised suburban network and the coal and livestock trains which keep the life of the community flowing.

Passenger

In many countries railways were introduced as mineral lines but speedily became popular for passenger transport. The first line in Scotland to be built with the authority of an Act of Parliament was the Kilmarnock and Troon Railway. This was visited by the French observer Dupin in 1817 who described the passenger traffic in these words: "I saw some diligences established on the iron railway"[1] while nine years later Duncan's *Itinerary of Scotland* says for the benefit of tourists: "Carriages made to run on the railway, pass once or twice a day to and from Troon, which has become a fashionable sea-bathing town."[2] Later lines, such as the Stockton and Darlington Railway, were constructed primarily for freight but the speed obtainable attracted passengers and the one which aroused public interest was the Liverpool and Manchester Railway. The faith of the engineers in the locomotive was justified and the service provided, two hours for the 30 miles between the two cities, meant that the trains were well patronized: £101,829 was received for passenger fares in the first year compared with an estimate of £10,000. From this experience

[1] C. Dupin, *Narratives of Two Excursions to the Ports of England, Scotland and Ireland*. London, c.1820, p. 47.
[2] Route No. 159.

149

financiers were encouraged to support lines which offered passenger traffic as the main inducement. The popularity by passengers was also experienced in the U.S.A. where there was a similar upsurge of movement. Before the railway linking Charleston and Hamburg (S.Ca.) was opened in 1835 the average monthly movement was 50 people; in the first six months after opening it averaged over 2,500. As each new line in the eastern states was opened there was the same explosive expansion and it was frequently found that, although the line might have been intended for freight transport, all the rolling stock had to be used to satisfy passenger demands.

When railways commenced running considerable distances longitudinally the matter of timekeeping became important; their coaching predecessors had always followed local time. Even the short longitudinal span of Britain meant that the G.W.R. had to allow for 10 minutes local time between London and Bristol: Greenwich Mean Time was only officially adopted in 1880 although the L.N.W.R. had adopted London time as standard in 1847. With continental distances American railways were more troubled but it was not until 1883 that standard time zones (Eastern, Central, Mountain and Pacific, each one hour apart) were introduced.

The first coaches were either simple boxes on a frame or, for the first-class, an adaptation of the bodies of horse-coaches. For the cheaper travel some of the earliest coaches lacked windows, and even doors, and, on occasion, holes were bored in the floor to allow the rain-water to run away. Dickens describes the American coaches in these terms:

"The cars are like shabby omnibuses, but larger: holding thirty, forty, fifty people. The seats, instead of stretching from end to end, are placed crosswise. Each seat holds two persons. There is a long row of them on each side of the caravan, a narrow passage up the middle, and a door at both ends. In the centre of the carriage there is usually a stove, fed with charcoal or anthracite coal; which is for the most part red-hot. It is insufferably close; and you see the hot air fluttering between you and any other object you may happen to look at, like the ghost of smoke."

The immigrant trains were at first very primitive but in the 1880s they were given slatted sleeping berths.

The weight of trains, per passenger seat, has greatly increased the burden on the locomotive. To reduce this burden experiments were made pre-war with welded construction and with change of design and the L.M.S.R. succeeded in reducing the weight per passenger-seat from 1,615 lb. to 1,385 lb. but British Railways after the war, by making the coaches more shock-proof, have increased the tare to 1,540 lb. Suburban coaches only average 660 lb. per passenger-seat, except for electric stock with motor-coaches, because of less luxury and the absence of heavy dining-cars.

Prestige is largely responsible for fast running. The expense of track maintenance, heavier fuel consumption and the disadvantage of heavy trains running on the same track at very different speeds has made railway operators, on occasion, reluctant to provide fast trains. Foxwell and Farrer by their writings[1] did much to educate the public to the value of fast trains. At the period of their examination of train speeds the authors regarded 40 m.p.h., including stops, as the definition of speed to qualify for express classification. In the summer of 1883 there were in the U.S.A. 13,956 miles run daily at about this express speed (the maximum was 43 m.p.h.), which compared with an express train mileage for the British Isles of 62,904. The Victorian world marvelled at these speeds and to them attributed the cheapening of commodities and the freer flow of ideas. In the inter-war period were a series of tests which were intended to pave the way for more rapid trains but the effects of the war and the introduction of diesel units have to some degree broken the continuity of the experiments. Immediately before the 1939–45 war the fastest booked European runs were:

Country	Route	Miles	Speed	Notes
Great Britain	King's Cross–Edinburgh	392¾	65·5	Steam
„ „	Swindon–Paddington	77¼	71·4	
France-Belgium	Paris–Brussels	193	64·4	„
Belgium	Brussels–Bruges	57·4	74·9	„
Germany	Berlin–Hanover	157·9	83·1	Diesel-Electric
„	Hamm–Hanover	109·7	83·3	„ „
„	Berlin–Hamburg	178·2	71·7	Steam

[1] E. Foxwell, "English Express Trains in 1883", *Stat. Soc. Jour.*, 1883; E. Foxwell and T. C. Farrer, *Express Trains, English and Foreign*. London, 1889.

The pre-war experiments, which demanded easy curves and improved track, may be illustrated by three outstanding records :

Year	Railway Route	Speed m.p.h.	Notes
1931	German State Hamburg–Berlin	95·7	Experimental coach driven by a propeller. Max. speed 143 m.p.h.
1938	L.N.E.R. Essendine Bank	126·0	Short burst of speed
1939	Italian State Florence–Milan	101·8	Electric, start-to-stop speed

After the war there was a remarkable recovery of train speeds and by 1953 a daily 23,889 train-miles were run in Europe at 62 m.p.h. or more : most of this must be credited to the French railway administration which made up two-thirds of the European total and so had greatly exceeded their pre-war position. In the Netherlands also had been a spectacular rehabilitation compared with the British and German. The fastest runs in Europe are by electric traction on the line between Paris and Lyon, covered in 1953 at an average speed of 77·1 m.p.h.[1]

The following Table summarizes the post-war position for fast European rail traffic and shows the amazing recovery in some of the countries which have had to re-equip owing to the ravages of war.

Electric			miles	m.p.h.
France ...	...	Paris–Lyon	317·4	77·1
Italy ...	...	Milan–Bologna	135·6	72·0
Switzerland	...	Nyons–Morges	16·1	69·0
Belgium	...	Brussels–Antwerp ...	27·5	66·0
Netherlands	...	Amsterdam–Utrecht ...	20·8	65·7
Sweden	...	Hassleholm–Eslov ...	31·0	64·1
Germany	...	Bremen–Rotenburg ...	26·5	63·6
Diesel				
France ...	...	Evreux–Bernay	32·1	68·8
Denmark	...	Roskilde–Slagelse	38·3	65·6

[1] In 1954 an electric train, with standard equipment, set up a world speed record of 151 m.p.h. between Dijon and Beaune and the following year 205·6 m.p.h. was attained between Lamothe and Morceux across the edge of the Landes.

Diesel			*miles*	*m.p.h.*
Germany	...	Freiburg–Offenburg ...	39·0	65·0
Italy ...	...	Fossano–Cavallarmaggiore	11·8	64·3
Steam				
U.K. ...	...	Paddington–Bristol ...	118·4	67·6
France ...	...	Chaumont–Vesoue ...	74·0	66·3

This Table, based on analyses published in the *Railway Magazine*, does not include all fast runs for each country but is restricted to the fastest for each method of haulage.

In North America remarkable accelerations have also been made to meet the competition from air transport. In addition to track improvements there has been a considerable track re-alignment. In the 1930s the New York Central rebuilt the track for 4½ miles through Syracuse on viaduct and embankment to replace the anachronism of street lines; before 1936 a hundred trains ran daily with a speed limit of 10 to 15 m.p.h. along 1½ miles of Washington Street. Dieselization has greatly speeded train times: the Union Pacific cut 16 hours off the journey time between Chicago and San Francisco while the C.P.R. cut 16 hours off the time between Montreal and Vancouver and saved a night on the journey.

Speeds cannot always be fast and in countries such as Northern Rhodesia, which in 1946 had a population of 22,000 Europeans spread over a quarter of a million square miles, stations are few and far between. From Livingstone and Ndola the stations are as follows with the mileages inserted between the station names: Livingstone – 53 miles – Zimba – 34 – Kalomo – 44 – Choma – 41 – Pemba – 23 – Monze – 37 – Mazabuka – 30 – Kafue – 29 – Lusaka – 29 – Chisamba – 39 – Broken Hill – 39 – Kapiri M'Poska – 82 – Ndola. Even unattended crossing loops are 10 to 15 miles apart and working demands rigid timekeeping. Passenger trains cannot be fast under these, or similar, circumstances and in 1940 it understandably took from Bulawayo 11 hours for the 297 miles to Salisbury, 35 hours for the 674 miles to Johannesburg, 37 hours for the 670 miles to Beira and 32 hours for the 777 miles to Ndola.

Passenger services can include a variety of activities and amenities not usually provided in a small country. On the Trans-Australian line a piano is installed to help while away the time but this pales beside some of the amenities on American expresses —radio, magazines, library, shorthand-typist, barber, ladies' maid, train-hostess, in addition to waiters and stewards. On the *Twentieth Century Limited* which runs daily in several sections between New York and Chicago, for every operating man other than the locomotive crew, there are ten people to attend to the comfort of the passengers.

Competition can stimulate the provision of services and these may become excessively generous and lead to a loss in operation. Examples might be drawn from all countries where there are alternative routes and where the administration is not a bureaucracy. One of the best examples of the solution which can be reached is seen in Canada where the C.P.R. and C.N.R. concerns compete for traffic at many points. In the west the routes are usually sufficiently separated not to cause intense competition whereas in the east they are parallel and close. In 1931 the two railways accelerated their service between Toronto and Montreal but, finding it unprofitable, agreed to organize the traffic and to pool rolling-stock and stations. The public has a more frequent service than before the outburst of competition.

The longest railway journey made by one train is that of the Trans-Siberian Express which takes nine days for the journey between Moscow and Vladivostock and although the train only runs three times a week nine train-sets are required as well as 20 for the daily slower train. The first through sleeping-car service across the U.S.A. was instituted in 1946; before then passengers had to change trains at Chicago or St. Louis. In Europe long-distance train operation was facilitated by the international groups which own rolling stock—*Wagons-Lits*, *Pullman* and *Mitropa*, the first operated also in China, Egypt and the Near East. The *Orient Express* (Calais–Istanbul) commenced running in 1883 and further services were added to meet new demands, for example in 1939 the *Taurus Express* (Haydarpasa–Ankara–Mosul–Baghdad) and in 1946 the *Nord Express* (Stockholm–Paris). War seriously disrupts these facilities and since 1945 *Wagons-Lits* have been almost entirely displaced from eastern Europe. In the northern hemisphere these long-distance expresses have played an important part in breaking the barrier of distance but now they are particularly vulnerable to air competition.

Passenger fares have an important effect upon population movements, their influence on the spread of London is considered on p. 168, but if low they can also help to reduce the sense of remoteness. In 1923 the return fare concession in Queensland allowed 1,000 miles of travel for 25s. 5d., i.e. ¼d. a mile, and this fare, for people living over 100 miles from the coast, was claimed as the cheapest in the world.

The passenger traffic of long-distance trains in the British Isles reveals a curious cycle through the week. The following statistics are based on three-monthly periods in winter and summer with 100 selected as the average for each class in each period. Monday is the busiest for first-class and Saturday the slackest whereas with third-class Saturday is the busiest day in summer and Monday in winter. There is food for thought as to the social implications of these pre-war statistics. Although a greater train-mileage is run in summer the trains are better filled and the receipts per train-mile are higher, a matter of importance to the management.

	WINTER		SUMMER	
	1st	3rd	1st	3rd
Monday	114	131	120	123
Tuesday	104	90	100	84
Wednesday	104	88	96	78
Thursday	103	86	100	83
Friday	111	103	109	104
Saturday	64	102	75	128

[Based on D. R. Lamb, Modern Railway Operation. London, 1941, pp. 182–3.]

Train Ferries

To avoid passengers having to change carriages and to avoid also the trans-shipment of freight, a number of railway administrations have provided train ferries to eliminate water breaks which cannot be bridged or tunnelled. Many of these ferries have their trips connecting with express trains. The operation of the service may be greatly facilitated in tideless seas such as the Baltic and the Mediterranean. The ferry across the Strait of Messina, operated since 1898, has been very valuable in promoting the development of Sicily while the ferries to the Danish archipelago and the Scandinavian peninsula have stimulated international trade. Ferry terminal points have to be more complicated to cope with the tidal range at or near the English Channel and their introduction was consequently delayed. The Harwich–Zeebrugge ferry-service, inaugurated in 1924, has proved valuable for freight, particularly agricultural produce.

Mails

From the early days of railway operation their services have been used by the Post Office. In addition to the use of ordinary passenger trains for conveying mails, special mail trains are run with equipment to pick up and discharge mail-pouches while travelling at speed. These special trains have coaches fitted for sorting the mails and are known as Travelling Post Offices. Until the railway had provided a rudimentary network it was impossible for the Post Office to organize the Penny Post because its financial success was contingent on a vast expansion in the numbers of letters carried and this quantity could never have been handled by the stage-coaches. Again the parcel service of the Post Office had to wait until the railway facilities were available.

In the United States the large-scale conveyance of mails also developed after the introduction of railways. William Fargo in 1844 organized, with Henry Wells, the first Express Company to operate west of Buffalo and in 1851 formed Wells, Fargo and Company to conduct the express business from New York to San Francisco *via* Panama, and in 1857 the Overland Mail Company to carry U.S. mails ; the Pony Express, inaugurated in 1860, charged, besides the U.S. postage, a dollar for a $\frac{1}{2}$ oz. letter. This expensive method could never meet the needs of an expanding community and as the railways extended they were at once used for mails particularly if they had been constructed with the aid of land-grants which were conditional on the carriage of mails at low rates. It was on the post-office network, which in turn depended upon the railways, that the well-known mail-order stores of cities such as Chicago came to depend.

Freight

At first the lines, whether built under private or State auspices, carried goods and passengers without reference to rivals but as the network grew so exchange equipment had to be provided.

The marshalling yard in various forms exists today on all railway systems. In essence it consists of a series of sidings through which freight wagons can be passed and be shuffled in the process into destination order. Marshalling yards are placed at strategic traffic nodes on a network. At first the yards were just parallel sidings worked by a locomotive moving trucks about so that not only did one siding contain all the trucks, brought in from all the feeding lines, destined for one route but also the trucks were arranged in order of stations along the route. This method is slow and expensive in locomotive- and man-power. In 1873 the L.N.W.R. were in difficulties over the marshalling of trains at Edge Hill, the yard which served the Liverpool Docks. Their engineer, Mr. Footner, used for the extension required an area which sloped down to the west and adapted the layout so the trucks could move by gravity. The sidings were arranged in the form of a pair of gridirons, each on a gradient of 1 in 80, so that by opening the correct points it was possible to lead the trucks forward in the desired order. An ingenious safety catch was invented to prevent runaways. This sorting by gravity was able to handle over 2,000 wagons a day and the technique was adopted elsewhere even though the lie of the land was not naturally suitable.

The modern approach is to build a hump sufficiently steep to get wagons moving freely and among many examples may be named Wath, Whitemoor, Feltham and Toton (in Britain), Hamm in Germany and in North America the great Potomac Yard[1] and the new C.P.R. Yard near Montreal. These yards have modern devices to expedite the working; for example, special braking bars (known in the U.S.A. as "car-retarders"), to control the speed of wagons according to their weight, electric or pneumatic operation of points, teleprinter outfits to codify and report instructions to key points and wireless for transmission of orders. These yards are often provided in open country because of the large area they require; fortunately the bomb-damage which allowed the construction of a large yard at Orleans is not normal,

[1] This yard in the southern outskirts of Washington, D.C., has 110 miles of track and a capacity of 8,168 cars a day. It is owned by the Fredricksburg and Potomac R.R. Co., which is the only U.S. company which has existed for over a century under the original name and without reorganization.

but they do expedite traffic so long as it does not have to be trans-shipped from the wagon. Freight rolling stock spends much of its time in terminals and yards—in Canada fifty per cent—and so every effort is made to speed traffic facilities, even at high cost.

Transit sheds serve in much the same way as marshalling yards but for the consignment less than a wagon-load. From the stations in an area, all the consignments going, say, towards the east are sent forward to the transit shed, again situated at a traffic node such as Crewe, where they are sorted and brought together by station of destination. While it gives additional labour it reduces haulage of partially loaded wagons and so helps to keep down operational costs.

Since 1930 the handling of freight has been reorganized in the Netherlands. The use of containers has been encouraged and the aim is to provide between any two communities of any size a 24-hour door-to-door service. This has meant faster trains and is achieved by dividing the country into 36 traffic zones, based on key stations such as Breda and Utrecht, and inter-zonal movement takes place by night. Similar developments are taking place in other countries. In the United States loaded lorries are carried by night between Chicago and St. Louis which allows the railway to participate in the long-distance haulage but leaves to the road-haulage company the function of gathering and distribution of the individual items.

Freight brings in more revenue to railways than the passenger services. The unit of work is the ton-mile, *i.e.* carrying one ton of freight one mile, and there has been a great increase in the haulage, with fluctuations due to trade conditions. This may be illustrated from the United States where for long the Government has compelled the companies to make elaborate statistical returns.

TON-MILES PER HEAD OF POPULATION

1867	285	1920	3,914
1880	645	1930	3,142
1890	1,211	1940	2,851
1900	1,863	1944	5,363
1910	2,773		

The year 1944 was a peak year with the enormous traffic to meet war needs and with the Panama Canal closed to commercial traffic. American railways run trains with much greater loads than the British, *e.g.* in 1935 734 tons and in 1945 1,129 tons as the *average* freight train. Length of haul is also greater in the U.S.A. and as locomotives have become more powerful so the haulage has increased; in 1905 238 miles, 1925 309 miles and 1945 458 miles. This increase has been accompanied by faster running; in 1920 a freight train in 24 hours travelled 247 miles whereas a quarter of a century later it travelled 377 miles.

For long the American railway companies have had a system of common-user for their freight-cars by which they can be loaded by any company but the owner obtains some revenue. In Europe the problem has been more difficult. Since the war the *Europ* wagon pool was formed with ten countries contributing 160,000 wagons which could be drawn on and this has halved the empty haulage on international traffic.

Freight costs are seen in the charge to the consumer and can powerfully affect industrial location and development although the charge paid may bear no direct ratio to the cost of working over the line on which the works are situated. It is not possible to obtain more than the average revenue per ton-mile and usually for the older industrial nations the costs are higher.

Country	Year	Average revenue per ton-mile in U.S. cents
Norway	1939	2·68
Great Britain	1937	2·41
Germany	1938	2·31
Denmark	1939	2·23
Australia	1938	2·13
France	1937	1·95
Italy	1938	1·69
Sweden	1939	1·42
South Africa	1940	1·38
India	1938	1·00
U.S.A.	1946	0·98
Canada	1943	0·95
Japan	1937	0·68

[Data from Assoc. Amer. R.R., 1947.]

Increase of freight hauled may prove an embarrassment to the management. In the early days of the Union of South Africa there was little traffic from the interior to the coast but a heavy inland movement and, because wagons frequently travelled empty, low rates were introduced for maize and minerals moving to the coast. These rates were profitable because the wagons had to be moved in any case but a large export developed and now empty trucks have to be hauled from the coast and the reason for the low rates has ceased. Another example of the troubles which may ensue from a traffic increase has occurred on the Kenya–Uganda line where the increase of freight—86 million ton-miles were hauled in May, 1950—has meant a problem over locomotive water-supply particularly between Mombasa and Nairobi.

Agricultural produce although it may be hauled in great quantities may not be a convenient freight for the railway—special terminal facilities such as grain elevators have to be provided, which cannot be used for other traffic, and refrigerated or heated vehicles may be needed. The crops are frequently seasonal and have to be moved quickly with a peak demand for the railway equipment which may remain idle for the rest of the year. Great cities need vast quantities of perishable produce and approximately 1,600 carloads of such produce enters New York daily: a carload of bananas is $12\frac{1}{4}$ tons, of citrus fruits $23\frac{1}{4}$ tons, of eggs $16\frac{1}{3}$ tons, of butter 19 tons. The first refrigerated beef was shipped east from Chicago in 1857 but fruit was not sent by refrigerated car until 1866. Florida oranges first entered the New York market by refrigerator car in 1886 and Californian in the following year. It is the refrigerator car which has given a nationwide market to the growers and made fresh food available at all seasons. Europe has, although not on such a great scale, similar refrigerator car services. To handle fruit from North Africa the French railway administration has constructed at Perpignan a large cold-storage plant with apparatus for pre-chilling of the vans.

In Australia livestock trains are a feature of the railway services. Since cattle and sheep have been conveyed by rail the losses have been greatly reduced. Lower rates are charged for moving store animals than for fat stock and still lower rates for removing livestock from a drought area or for taking in fodder. Some of the livestock trains are enormous; a sheep train, for example, will carry 7,000 sheep. Railway rates are extremely difficult to levy equitably and in the case of the Australian state railways it is sometimes argued that the agricultural community is receiving a subsidy from the general user : in Western Australia in 1926 agricultural produce was responsible for 38·6 per cent of the ton-miles and 19·9 per cent of the revenue whereas general freight 6·0 per cent of the ton-miles but 20·5 per cent of the revenue.

Fish is another commodity which demands special facilities for transport : with its perishable nature speed and control of the temperature are essential. Fish is sent alive in special tank vans from Scandinavia to Germany while in Japan live carp are sent from Lake Biwa to Tokyo. Dead fish need either refrigerator vans or salt and ice to preserve the load. Refrigeration offers a more satisfactory control than ice because the temperature can be adjusted and the contents kept chilled if the train be delayed. Fish trains are frequently run express ; a well-known long distance fish special is that from Aberdeen to London which travels as fast as the passenger expresses.

Mineral workings often depend upon the provision of railways while the haulage of ores, or coal, together with the supplies required for mining, are an important element in the working arrangements of many lines. Mineral trains in Britain are composed of small wagons but while there have been attempts to increase their size it is unlikely that the large American type will ever be introduced. The savings with larger, non-bogie trucks are considerable both in the reduction of train length and in the haulage of dead-weight. For example with a pay-load of 600 tons :

			Wagons	
		10-ton	12-ton	20-ton
No. of wagons required ...	...	60	50	30
Length of train, ft.	... ...	1,080	975	735
Tare weight, tons	... ...	369	350	288
Gross weight, tons	... ...	969	950	888
% payload of gross weight	...	62	63	69

The great weight of coal produced from large collieries means mass movement and coal trains have been responsible for the

L

design of many large locomotives in order to keep the traffic moving. One example is the large Beyer-Garratt engines introduced to work the coal trains on the long ascent from Durban to Cato Ridge on the Pietermaritzburg line. The Witbank–Germiston line serves many collieries in its 80 miles and the average time for the 1,490 tons coal-trains is 4½ hours. This traffic is so substantial that in 1955 a new line was being constructed from Springs to Natalspruit in order to by-pass Johannesburg. The heavy cost of such capital works can be justified by the saving of time and the increased haulage which may be made possible with the same man-power.

The ability to move coal in mass provides a valuable payload for railways and at the same time stimulates industrial development which gives rise to further traffic. Exploitation on a large scale of the Copperbelt of Northern Rhodesia did not commence until the 1930s and it proved the basis of expansion of traffic on the Rhodesia Railways. This traffic increase has created serious problems for the railway management. Between 1947 and 1953–4 the freight hauled more than doubled and so strained the carrying capacity of the line that the management, to enable the Copperbelt to receive sufficient coal, placed goods traffic on the roads. There has had to be considerable capital investments to increase the capacity of the line, and, with limited financial resources, the supply of capital for rolling stock has been restricted; in 1955 it was announced that one of the major coppermining syndicates would provide, for hire to the Rhodesia Railways, a large number of wagons.

Many examples could be selected of the value of railways for the exploitation of minerals—manganese ore of the Gold Coast, phosphates of Tunisia, chrome ore in Rhodesia, iron ore in northern Sweden—but without hesitation it may be claimed that railways, in return, provide for many sites the most convenient medium of transport. Rivals do exist—water routes, aerial ropeway, road and pipe-line—but all lack some of the advantages of the rail. Petroleum used to be carried in bulk by tank-wagons but now, whenever the quantities justify, the pipe-line is substituted because of its advantages for the rapid and safe transport of mineral oil. Inspired by the success of the pipe-line for oil experiments have been made in America on the transport of coal, in suspension, along a pipe. When, as in Britain, freight rates are high encouragement is given to finding alternatives. Continental engineers are examining in detail the cost margins between hauling the coal to the consumer and transforming it into electricity and sending the power to the consuming points : the economic balance between costs of haulage and the losses on transmission of electricity varies with the calorific value of the coal in relation to the rates charged by rail. The real cost of rail transport is unmeasurable and the charge to the consumer is the only measure which is significant. Apparently trivial differentials may swing the traffic one way or another; one example which may be cited is that publicized in 1953 when the Port Authority of New York claimed that the import of iron ore at New York was being restricted because the rail charges were 66 cents a ton higher than those for Baltimore and that, with the increase expected in iron ore imports into the United States, this had now become a matter of moment.

CHAPTER VIII

THE URBAN PATTERN

THE provision of railways offers particular problems in urban districts but fortunately many of the lines constructed preceded the urban sprawl which has characterized the twentieth century. Within most cities natural slopes are not so severe as to be a constructional handicap but awkward gradients can occur because of the difficulty of crossing within short distances obstacles such as canals, rivers and roads: for example, when the London and North Western and Midland Railways were approaching their termini in London the Regent's Canal necessitated inconvenient slopes. In this review of some of the features of urban railways attention will first be directed to London, with particular reference to the passenger services, to Paris and to New York before summarizing the features which may be taken as characteristic of an urban system.

Sekon in his volume *Locomotion in Victorian London*[1] presents a fascinating picture of the successive improvements in the provision of transport in the great urban sprawl of London. When men walked to work their homes were within a narrow radius included in the territory from Highgate to Clapham and from Kensington to Bow. Inside this district certain areas were avoided, either because of the absence of bridges across the Thames or Regent's Canal or because while there might be a bridge the toll restricted its use—the only toll-free bridges within the London district were London Bridge, Blackfriars Bridge and Westminster Bridge and settlement tended to spread along the roads connecting with these free bridges at the expense of other sites.

Urban railways can be of four types: surface, elevated, shallow tunnel (cut-and-cover) and deep tube railways and London can offer examples of all types. The first London line opened was the elevated viaduct route from London Bridge to Greenwich which was completed as far as Deptford in 1836 and to Greenwich in 1838. In order to increase traffic the company advertised "free

[1] G. A. Sekon, *Locomotion in Victorian London*. Oxford, 1938.

tickets" available for three months' travel and these are the first recorded season-tickets. The second line to be opened was a normal surface line from Euston towards Birmingham. Opened in 1837 this company disdained the suburban traveller and for several years its first station was at Harrow, 11½ miles from the terminus. Services on these early lines were meagre. The network of surface lines was completed largely as the result of an outburst of enthusiasm for suburban railway construction in the 'fifties and 'sixties when the rivalry of the various companies provided alternative routes to many districts.

In 1845 there were no less than nineteen Bills deposited for railways in the metropolitan area and a Royal Commission was appointed to consider the situation. Among the schemes adversely reported upon was that of Charles Pearson who suggested a covered line to extend to a central terminus at Farringdon Street. A later Bill, largely through Pearson's enthusiasm, was successful and work commenced in 1860 on the first of the covered lines. The method of construction was largely by cut-and-cover because, with shallow lines following streets, it was easier than trying expensive and time-consuming tunnelling.[1] The first section was from Paddington to Farringdon Street and cost £186,000 a mile for the structural works. Extensions were rapidly proposed and the "Circle" route, the first of its kind in the world, was completed in 1871. The natural surface of the ground has largely disappeared but the profile of this shallow railway reflects the present surface and has on occasion, for example near Farringdon Street, had to enter made ground instead of being in the alluvial gravels. Most of the former river courses which were crossed had been turned into sewers and the largest of these, the Fleet, burst its retaining brick walls and flooded a section of the works with sewage. The Inner Circle rises towards the north and the depth of the metals below the ground level varies from 9 ft. to 65 ft. Great difficulty was experienced in some sections from the water contained in the sands, in the mobility of the London Clay and the liability to settlement of valuable buildings when the water drains away from the subsoil.

---

[1] For accounts of the engineering problems see B. Baker, *The Metropolitan and Metropolitan District Railways*, and J. W. Barry, *The City Lines and Extensions*. P.I.C.E., lxxxi, 1885.

It had been intended that the traffic would be handled by locomotives without a firebox which would have to rely on stored steam to maintain a service of five to ten minutes' interval. This method was found unsatisfactory and the use of locomotives with a condenser was tried. As traffic increased and as coke was replaced by coal the atmosphere became intolerable : contemporary issues of *Punch* present an impression of the inferno of the Circle line although "blow-holes" were provided to allow the smoke to escape along with the sulphur fumes which irritated the lungs and eyes. These shallow underground railways supplied a real necessity in the life of the metropolis and their popularity was immedate and great.

In 1890 the fourth method of railway for urban use was opened : the tiny City and South London Railway which ran three miles to Stockwell inaugurated the system of modern "tubes" which depend on electricity. These tubes, bored through the London Clay, are easy to construct in the sense that the engineer is not tied by surface inequalities and is not caught in the medley of underground pipes and sewers which criss-cross a modern city. Their construction is extremely expensive and is justified only by a large traffic potential.

On the basis of these four types of construction London is now provided with a network of lines which is unique in its intricacy (Figure 5).

Trains and services in themselves may not greatly affect a community but owing to a series of legal enactments, of which the most significant was the *Cheap Trains Act* of 1883, the railways which served London were instrumental in the spread of the urban area. The early Act of 1844 by which all passenger-carrying lines had to run at least one train a day, stopping at all stations but maintaining an average speed of 12 m.p.h., did not benefit the suburban dweller. When an extension of the metropolitan lines of London, Chatham and Dover Railway was being considered by Parliament the company, to counter opposition because they were destroying many houses, volunteered to run trains at hours and fares convenient to workmen. The Metropolitan Railway introduced such concessions in 1864[1] and the following year they

[1] For details of fare concessions see C. E. Lee, *Passenger Class Distinctions.* London, 1946.

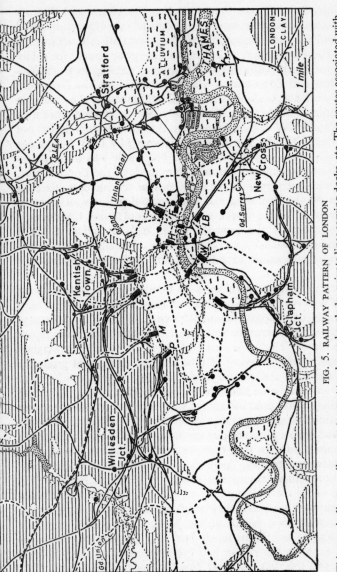

FIG. 5. RAILWAY PATTERN OF LONDON

This map indicates railway routes, not tracks, and excludes private lines serving docks, etc. The routes associated with the Underground system are indicated by pecked lines. The rectangles indicate the passenger termini, the large dots goods depots, and the small dots coal depots. The unshaded areas are terrace deposits.

C: Cannon Street
E: Euston
F: Fenchurch Street
H: Holborn
K: King's Cross
L: Liverpool Street
L.B.: London Bridge
M: Marylebone
P: Paddington
S: St. Pancras
V: Victoria
W: Waterloo
X: Charing Cross

were introduced for the line connecting Blackfriars and Victoria *via* Brixton. Similar clauses were introduced into other companies' Acts and the most important of these was that authorizing the Great Eastern Railway to extend to Liverpool Street: for a fare of 2*d*. return the company had to convey passengers from Walthamstow and Edmonton to the terminus. These low fares were appreciated and undoubtedly contributed much to the extension of London towards the north-east. By 1913 there were more than 500 trains a day carrying workmen into the metropolis for not more than 2*d*. a day for the return journey: by 1938 the average workman's fare was still under 4*d*. The traffic was immense, in 1937 about 140 million journeys were made in the London area, but it was not very remunerative because the increase placed a burden on the operating and had demanded line-widenings on some routes. Traffic working into Liverpool Street had become complex because the crowded trains had to arrive within a short time of each other. With change of social habits it was no longer reasonable to provide trains arriving at about 6.30 a.m.

Along the lines of railways in London many stations were created to serve the built-up areas but these, while they might have been justified in the days of horse-drawn omnibuses, lost patronage when the electric tramcars and the internal-combustion omnibuses were adopted. The convenience of the street vehicle outweighed any possible slight saving of time and the companies gradually closed the inner stations. Beyond about four miles the advantage of rail speed became appreciable and, by closing the inner ring of stations, this speed advantage was increased at the time road congestion was slowing tram and bus traffic. South of the Thames there had been a group of pugnacious companies which had, with little opportunity for long-distance traffic, been forced to develop their suburban traffics. There had been much waste with needlessly competitive routes but when the Southern Railway was formed under the Railways Act of 1921 the company acquired a dense network on which they could organize interlocking electric suburban services. North of the Thames the rivalry over line construction had been much less, largely because the companies crossing the region had been interested in long-distance traffic, and this left the field free for underground lines. This accounts for the comparative absence of such lines south of the river.

The rail services drew within the zone of influence of an urban centre scattered settlements which might be completely separated by agricultural areas. Such an inclusion occurred in south-east England where towns, which were once so remote from the metropolitan influence that they led their own lives, became fused into the metropolitan district and developed as dormitories for the major centre. In many respects towns such as Dorking, Guildford, Brighton, Watford and St. Albans may be regarded as now very much influenced by the metropolis.

The situation in Paris differs from that in London largely because the Parisian has shown a marked reluctance to live far from the centre : before the war about 42 per cent of the Paris population lived within five kilometres ($3\frac{1}{8}$ miles) of the city centre compared with about 30 per cent for London and only 5 per cent for New York. In 1863 one railway ran workmen's trains at very cheap fares into Paris but then, as now, it was found that the Parisian workman would not live far from his work. In the nineteenth century the railways in Paris were exclusively radial except for the belt-lines which encircled the city. With the opening in 1900 of the *Métro* line from Porte Maillot to Porte de Vincennes came the first railway across the city. This opening was followed by a period of rapid construction during which the city became traversed by nine transverse, three radial and two circle passenger lines with numberous interchange points. The effectiveness of this network is increased by the stations being, on the average, only a third of a mile apart, and the pattern such that no part of the city is more than a quarter of a mile from an underground station. This metropolitan system is among the most intensively worked in the world. Most of the mileage, unlike that of London, is in shallow tunnels which can be readily reached by the passengers. The stations which are deepest, comparable with those under the heights of Hampstead in London, are under the heights of Montmartre and Chaumont where to have followed the surface closely would have increased the gradients.

When the Paris radial lines were being laid down branches were provided along the line of the old fortifications and these branches, joined one to another, besides linking adjacent radii have become of value as a belt-line (known as the *Petite Ceinture*). As with similar inner belt connections of London this belt-line lost much of its significance with the development of road transport but it is still used for trains linking the Gare du Nord and Gare de Lyon and so plays a part in long-distance traffic. Beyond the inner belt-line is the *Grande Ceinture* which functions almost exclusively for the transfer of freight traffic from one radial line to another and hence is associated with the principal marshalling yards. Knowledge of the functions of a railway in the life of a city such as Paris has been enriched by the unique geographical study, R. Clozier, *La Gare du Nord*, (Paris, 1940).

In New York the peculiarities of the site affect profoundly the pattern and nature of the railways. With the core of the city on Manhattan Island entrance from the west is barred by the deep and broad trench of the Hudson and a number of railways for long have been halted on the New Jersey side and forced to rely on ferries to carry vehicles across (*see* Fig. 6). The Pennsylvanian line managed to complete its tunnel into the city in 1910. Under the conditions which prevail in the New York district, the main-line companies cannot compete for local traffic and both elevated and underground (subway) routes are provided to meet local needs. The first elevated section was opened in 1878 and for a period these routes, four in Manhattan Island and more in Brooklyn, gave a frequent service on three tracks (the central track being used for business expresses towards the city during the morning rush and homeward in the evening). Constructed on girders running over the streets, at first worked by steam but later electrified, the "L" lines, as they are known colloquially, were noisy and disfiguring and the last was abandoned in 1955: the routes of some sections have been adapted for special car "speedways". In addition to the elevated lines the subways, hewn out of solid rock and then covered over to form a street, provide a shallow network. Most of the lines have four tracks, two for stopping trains and two for limited stops only. The costs of operation are kept down by "flat-rate" fares.

New York was the first area in the world to replace steam operation by all-electric. In 1902, two years after the greatly enlarged New York Central station had been completed, there was a bad accident which was attributed to smoke from locomotives and

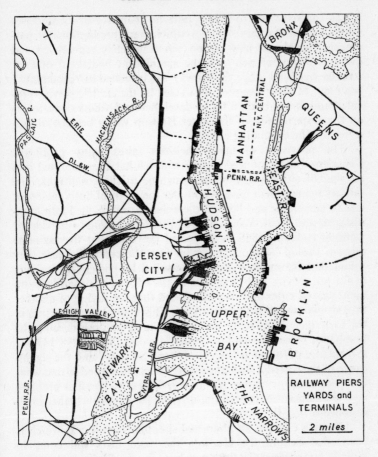

FIG. 6. RAILWAY PATTERN OF NEW YORK CITY AREA
[Based on map by Port of New York Authority]

Railway-owned property (routes, yards, and piers) are shown in black with
lines in tunnel pecked. The underground passenger system is not indicated.
The barrier of the Hudson estuary is emphasized by the great number of
railway terminals on the New Jersey side of the river.

it was enacted that from July 1908 no more steam locomotives were to enter the city on lines which were predominantly passenger. The almost new station was completely remodelled and over the new approach lines the magnificent boulevard of Park Avenue was built while the railway was extended in "catacombs" hewn out of the living rock. Attracted by the electric service provided an outer suburban traffic developed and villages and towns on the eastern bank of the lower Hudson valley became dormitories for the expanding city.

The provision of urban facilities raises many problems. Experience had produced a pattern which has been adopted in a number of cities with modifications due to site conditions. The railway management have to consider the needs of both passenger and freight traffic and both of these may be subdivided into long-distance and local. When the Royal Commissioners considered London traffic in 1846 they rejected the view that the mainline termini should be brought further into the centre because they found that the average distance travelled by passengers arriving at Euston, which had been sited at the edge of the then built-up area, was 64 miles and they concluded that the saving of another mile or two was of little importance. This might have been true in the early days of railways but during the succeeding decades the number of passengers had increased—on one day in 1898 133,481 arrived and departed at Liverpool Street Station—and the significance of the traveller from the outer suburbs increased so that what had been a minor matter became a serious one. The first problem then is to organize dispersal of arriving passengers whether long-distance or local.

Unless a city has an abnormal site, like New York, which is barricaded behind the Hudson, the main lines will come in radially and these radial lines may be few, as in Berlin, or as many as fifteen as in London. With the expense of entering the valuable central property the termini will tend to be grouped round the centre and the obvious way to link is by connecting peripheral branches to construct a belt-line encircling the urban sprawl and joining all the radii. This plan has been followed in a number of cities. Paris provides the best example with its *Petite Ceinture* and a less symmetrical vesion is found in London. If the belt-line is sufficiently close to the termini it can be of value for passenger connections but with improved street transport and underground rail-links most of the belt-line passenger services have been abandoned because the mileage traversed becomes excessive. Unfortunately if the belt-line is close in to the termini it cuts, where it is most congested, the flow of traffic, and so frequently an outer belt-line is provided by which, in particular, freight traffic can be kept off the routes most in demand for passenger services. Again Paris provides the best example with the *Grande Ceinture* and it is logical that near the intersection of the outer belt-line and the radii should be located the marshalling yards and the large goods depots.

The quantities of freight required to keep a large urban unit active are tremendous and the situation is complicated in the older cities by continued use of the traditional centres where the produce required by the citizens is sold wholesale. Ancient markets, such as Billingsgate and Covent Garden, might have been well located in relation to river or road transport for feeding a small city but, with the increase of population and the need to bring in ever greater quantities of fresh food, the fact that the railways could not readily approach such centres placed a needless burden on the roads. Smithfield was linked with the railways and there was also the scheme of the City of London to place the abattoirs at the Caledonian Market. Each of the companies which entered London had goods stations along their own metals and, in addition, the northern "coal lines" had coal depots alongside some of the southern lines; the multiplication of goods stations resulted in needless congestion of the roads because packages would be sent to the nearest depot owned by the company and not necessarily to the depot nearest physically. A. W. Gattie proposed before World War I that there should be a Central Goods Clearing House located in Clerkenwell and connected by underground railways able to take full-loading gauge rolling stock. The proposed clearing house was to cover 30 acres and to have four floors devoted to sorting of goods. Where possible goods were to be carried in containers, to reduce individual handling, and conveyor belts and lifts were to be freely used.[1] The new underground links were to connect with the existing underground Metropolitan lines at

[1] For an exposition, fully illustrated, of this proposal, see R. Horniman, *How to make the railways pay for the war*. London, 1919.

St. Pancras and Snow Hill together with a spur to Bishopsgate Street Station, and in this way link all the main radial lines north and south of the Thames. The scheme had many advantages but it is doubtful if the goods could be handled as expeditiously as Gattie believed.

In response to the geographical factors there is a certain modification of the "ideal" pattern for urban services,[1] but to modifications induced by the physical environment have been added those in response to ownership. Some cities have had their pattern provided by private enterprise while others have had, from the beginning, the local authority exercising a planning control even if not performing the actual operating of the services. Part of the difficulty has been the expense of providing the facilities either because of the cost of actual construction or because of the massive destruction of existing property. In Brussels, for example, it was desired to link the Nord and Midi stations and although the work on the impressive junction line commenced in 1911 it was not brought into use until 1952. The modern tendency, as found in London, Paris and New York, is for the various privately owned rivals to be fused into a public utility monopoly and to co-ordinate all the services whether by road or rail.

As from January 1st, 1948, the company working the railway and omnibus services of Paris handed its physical assets over to a public utility organization and the directors of the company decided to capitalize their accumulated experience in the handling of urban traffic by creating an advisory service for cities experiencing traffic problems. Within a few years the experts had studied conditions in Montevideo, Calcutta, Rio de Janeiro, Santo Paulo and Montreal. Soil, slope and population conditions were examined by teams of experts sent to the cities by the company and their surveys should result in French engineering products finding a wider market.

Underground railways attract municipalities faced with congestion on the streets but the cost of construction is a deterrent. The 1950 Report by Sir William Halcrow and J. P. Thomas on a scheme for an underground railway in Auckland gives interesting comparisons of the cost of tunnelling. Taking 100 as the cheapest London prices :

[1] S. H. Beaver, "The railways of great cities". *Geography*, June 1937.

Single tube, double track for tube rolling stock ... 100
14 ft. 6 in. circular tunnel for tube rolling stock ... 119
Twin 12 ft. 6 in. tunnels for London Metro. stock ... 125
Single tunnel, double track for N.Z. goods profile ... 131
Twin tunnels 15 ft. 2 in. wide 141
Twin tunnels 16 ft. 6 in. circular 154
Twin tunnels 19 ft. 6 in. circular 175

The cost of the extension of the underground line to connect Victoria, *via* Euston and Highbury, with Walthamstow was estimated in 1955 to cost £5 million a mile. Such schemes cannot be undertaken lightly.

A number of cities are considering plans for improving their cross-city links and the Table summarizes the situation for some of these where the underground system is already sufficiently extensive to make a real contribution to the movement of passengers across the city and facilitate dispersal to the homes, offices and factories.

DETAILS OF SOME URBAN SYSTEMS ASSOCIATED WITH UNDERGROUND RAILWAYS

		Route length, miles	Average distance stations apart, miles	Passengers per mile per year, million	Year first section opened
London	... ...	248	0·8	2·3	1863
Paris ...	... ...	117	0·3	9·1	1900
Berlin	... ...	50	0·5	2·6	1902
Moscow	... ...	37	1·0	22·8	1935
Madrid	... ...	11	0·4	31·6	1919
New York	... ...	241	0·5	6·5	1878
Philadelphia ...	...	29	0·5	6·0	1908
Chicago	... ...	90	0·5	1·6	1943*
Buenos Aires	...	18	0·4	16·6	1913
Tokyo	... ...	12	0·6	10·0	1927

* Before the opening of the first underground line in 1943 Chicago had a number of elevated lines which are now worked in conjunction with the subway. [Based on H. Sampson, *World Railways*, 1954–55. London.]

These electrified systems are mainly devoted to passenger movement but there are also some, such as the well-known Chicago Freight Tunnel System, which are devoted to the cross-city movement of goods. This 60 miles long freight line links the main line goods stations with factories and warehouses but is only large enough to take 2 ft. 6 in. gauge metals and so does not provide through-running facilities.

Upon the efficiency of the traffic arteries depends the well-being of the larger urban units and while road transport can satisfy many needs the railway has hitherto proved the best agent for the mass movements of passengers and goods. Within the hinterland of a city, as with a port, the transport must be intricate and adaptable reaching out to all centres participating in the life of the region. The fact of having brought these people and goods by mass movement into the nodal points of the city immediately raises problems of which the greatest is that of re-dispersal to the destination points. Congestion must remain at key times but the maximum demand during the working day does in large measure control the extent of the facilities. It is the lack of appreciable use of these during the slack periods which makes it so very difficult for the urban systems to remain solvent. Without electricity no urban area could operate its peak railway traffic with efficiency, ease and cleanliness—witness the public dismay at the conditions which prevail in the two steam-operated lines which cross Glasgow by shallow tunnels—and it may be fairly claimed that the railways now generally perform the task more effectively than they did at the beginning of the century.

CHAPTER IX

RIVALS TO THE RAIL

FOR a period in the late nineteenth century railways, in many countries, had a virtual monopoly of transport and much of the legislation has been devoted to curbing the powers of the monopolists. Although conditions have changed in this century appreciation of the new status was slow in coming and even the 1921 Railways Act in Britain contained clauses on charging powers which still assumed monopoly conditions. This chapter will discuss the relation of the railways to other transport media and an emphasis will be given to the situation in the British Isles because it serves to illustrate a number of principles. Within the limited compass of this volume it is impossible to correlate all the rivalries which exist and to detail the methods by which the railway services have been attacked and how the managements have retaliated in their attempts to retain traffic. Where appropriate the routes between London and Edinburgh will be selected to illustrate the competition which has prevailed. Between these two capitals all forms of transport, except canal, contribute to the rivalry.

Before discussing the competition which exists, the burdens borne by the railway management and which are irrespective of the operating of the trains, should be noted. In 1930 the capital cost of the railway track in Britain was estimated at £800 million and the annual charge, if interest was paid at $4\frac{1}{2}$ per cent, was £36 million, maintenance and renewal costs were £18 million, signalling charges £6½ million and rates paid to local authorities £3½ million which gave a total annual burden of £64 million. Road users were, instead of paying for the capital cost of their road, enjoying a substantial legacy from the past and the findings of the Salter Conference on Rail and Road in 1932 suggested that an annual charge of £60 million a year would be a fair burden on road users and that it should be based essentially on ton-mileage of the vehicles. In 1938 motor taxation brought in £88 million but a proportion of this was in the nature of a sumptuary tax on private cars, and thus did not bear on commercial road services. Immediately before the 1939–45 war the railway track costs amounted to some 34 per cent of receipts whereas for commercial road vehicles licence and petrol tax was only 13 per cent. Railway companies in the United States have also complained of the incidence of taxation : in 1925 they worked for 22 days to pay their taxes, in 1935 25 days and in 1945 34 days, and in 1950 46 days, which has since decreased to the 1945 position. Until 1929 railway companies in Britain paid 5 per cent duty on all passenger fares above third class but in return for capital expenditure of £7 million, the then estimated capitalization value, the duty was abolished.

The basis of railway charges has long been controversial and legislation has assumed that, in view of the monopoly character of the companies in their function of common carriers, it was essential that there should be restrictive enactments and Parliament applied the principle of maximum charges as had been laid down for canals. The companies had lower rates for large users but in effect the charge was not based on the cost of transport but on what the traffic would bear : a ton of gold would be charged at a higher rate than a ton of scrap iron although it was a far less awkward load. The 1921 Railway Act substituted for the principle of maximum charges that of published "standard charges" but by 1938 over four-fifths of the traffic was at "exceptional rates" which the companies had been forced to allow or else see the traffic move to the roads. The Report of the Royal Commission on Transport in 1930 declared that it was not in the national interest to drive further heavy traffic from the railways to the roads but, as the lighter and more valuable traffic went, the railways were left with a larger proportion of the bulky and less profitable movement. An example, which was freely quoted, was that of crated goods being sent by road but the empty crates being returned by rail. By the Transport Act of 1953 integration, as had been pursued under the Transport Act of 1947, was abandoned and the new Act replaced it by competition. For the first time the railway management were given the power to agree with a trader for the rates at which traffic would be conveyed and there was no obligation to publish the rate. In the draft scheme announced in 1954 the Commission summarized the basis of the new charging system as being what the job cost to perform and what the competitive market (and *not* the traffic) would bear. The first factor is a most important divergence from historical methods of charging—for the first time charges will be related to the character of the traffic as regards loadability, the operating conditions over the individual route, the degree of balanced loading and the intensity of competition. It will take many years for the full force of this new rating principle to be realized but it should result in the geographical factors which affected the construction and operation of the route being reflected in the charge to the user of transport. No longer will distance be the sole criterion for goods within the same classification group.

Road Competition

When the railway companies started operation the existing road transport services disappeared because, despite any nostalgic sentiment, it was so much more convenient and cheaper to travel by rail than by road. In 1658 an early stage coach was running between London and Edinburgh and took 13 days on the journey, which time was slightly reduced until 1776 when a "flying coach" reduced the time to four days for the 391 miles. In the 1830s, with improved roads and coaches, the journey took only 42 hours 23 minutes. When the rail route between London and Edinburgh was from Euston *via* Rugby, Derby and York the journey time was $12\frac{1}{2}$ hours but with competition, as new lines were opened and the rail distance reduced to 393 miles, the time became only 10 hours. The years 1888 and 1895 saw intense competition between the east and west coast groups and Edinburgh was reached in 6 hours 19 minutes from London, but thereafter came agreements and the time was fixed 8 hours 15 minutes for the shortest route until 1932 when it was reduced to 7 hours 45 minutes. The *Coronation* limited train introduced in 1937 took only 6 hours. The desire for speed caused the death of the early British road services which, in their day, were the finest in the world.

The twentieth century brought new competition on the roads. The first through motor coach between London and Edinburgh ran in 1928, the time of arrival was not announced, and the present service evolved with a journey time of 15 hours; although this doubled the time taken by rail the fare is under half. The specific operating cost of a long-distance coach is less than that of a train but the operating cost per seat is higher per mile. To carry

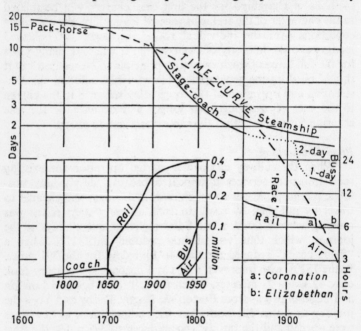

FIG. 7. THE JOURNEY TIME LONDON–EDINBURGH

[Based, with permission, on diagrams by P. G. Masefield, Presidential Address to the Institute of Transport, 1955]

Both sets of graphs are on logarithmic scales. The larger set shows the progressive reduction in time by the East Coast route from pack-horse travel to air, with the times based on the journey to the centres of the cities. The inset indicates the approximate numbers travelling by each of the transport agents.

a thousand persons between Edinburgh and London the cost, but not the charge, would be less by rail than road for the journey. The overhead charges of the rail cannot be quickly reduced if traffic is not coming forward whereas those of the coach operators are in closer relationship to the traffic carried. Much of the rail equipment is geared to peak demands and with immobile equipment it is useless at other times and thus the profits on working at the peak periods have to cover also a proportion of the slack period expenses. Track, signalling and telecommunication systems, stations, warehouses and yards as well as locomotives and rolling stock have to be maintained for the occasional use.

Road systems are instrinsically more useful than railway tracks. Every trader has a road to his premises and more homes are better approached by road than from a railway station. An excellent example of how the road defeated the rail, despite excellent services on the latter, is the struggle for traffic in the district round Aberdeen. In the 6¼ miles north to Dyce and in the 7⅜ miles west to Culter were eight and nine intermediate stations respectively and there were 21 trains daily in each direction which performed the journeys expeditiously. With the opening of tram routes parallel to the railways for part of the distance and the provision of bus services for the whole distance these suburban rail services had to be withdrawn just before World War II because of lack of patronage although the railway stations were within a stone's throw of the main roads along which there was ribbon development. Tramcars and, later, omnibuses have led to the closing of many stations as well as branch lines in the country.

Water Competition

Water competition may be divided into two categories—sea and canal, lake or river. Sea competition can be a very real one to railways because a modern cargo ship can carry great quantities for a fifth of the rates for railways but the conditions are not always favourable for the sea. In a country such as Britain while a 12-knots vessel may perform the journey between London and Leith in 33 hours, the sea distance is 495 miles, there is the difficulty of tidal ports and it is not easy to arrange for regular sailings and arrivals. Since the war most of the passenger ship sailings coastwise about the British Isles have been abandoned and it is only with connections to islands that the services still continue almost unabated.

Canals do not possess all the advantages of railways—they may be closed by the weather, ice or shortage of water—and have the major drawback of not being able to enter easily to industrial premises. The existence of a canal, with the threat that if rates are too high by rail the water link will be used, serves to keep down rail charges. The Erie Canal linking the Hudson valley with the interior has had an influence in this way far beyond the tonnage of goods that the canal actually carries. American railroads have had to introduce lower rates where water competition is possible. In Britain, competition from canals is not active, partly because many of the canals are moribund for want of capital improvements, and partly because they cannot take the large modern barge which can carry an economic load. The following statistics are undoubtedly too favourable to the railway because terminal charges are an important section of rail charges but they do suggest the relative position of water, road and rail as competitors for traffic.

CONVEYANCE COSTS, EXCLUDING TERMINALS
[Based on E. Short, *Railways and the State*, London, 1946, p. 23.]

	Payload (tons)	Cost per ton-mile assuming 50% payload
Canal: 40-ton motor barge drawing 40-ton barge	80	0·62d.
Road: 15-ton lorry	15	1·52d.
Rail	522	0·32d.

The demands of the canal transport for man-power are intermediate between the road and the rail: for 500 tons the road would require 34 power units with driving crews whereas the rail could haul with three men. The canal would require six or seven barge crews.

It is frequently declared that the railway companies in Britain strangled canal traffic. This is an overstatement because the canal proprietors frequently demanded the purchase of the waterway, as the price for withdrawing Parliamentary opposition, and the railway companies continued to pay dividends on the purchase price. E. A. Pratt in his detailed record of canals in Scotland states the case very clearly when he shows how, after the purchase of the Forth and Clyde Canal, the North British Railway ran branches to tap this canal traffic and the new owners of the canal, the Caledonian Railway, were forced, in self-defence, to provide lines competing with their own waterway.[1]

Air Competition

This competition is very much of the last two decades. On June 13th, 1910, an aeroplane was flown from New York City to Philadelphia on the first announced schedule. The following year Rodgers flew across the U.S.A. from the Atlantic to the Pacific seaboard, in an actual flying time of about 82 hours—he made many stops—at an average speed, excluding stops, of $51\frac{1}{2}$ m.p.h. This was the first transcontinental journey by air. America, land of vast distances, was quick to seize on this new time-saver. Internal air services in Britain were slower in being accepted and the first regular service between London and Edinburgh was only established in 1938 with a journey time of about $4\frac{1}{4}$ hours. Since the war improved aircraft have been used and the journey time is about $3\frac{1}{2}$ hours, of which only $1\frac{1}{2}$ hours is in the air and the rest of the time is spent in travelling between the centres of the cities and the airports. It is anticipated that newer turbo-prop aircraft, to be introduced shortly, will cut the journey by nearly half an hour.

On speed aircraft have the advantage over the railway but it is not one-sided because the payload is small with aircraft and running costs are high. For the same expenditure a railway can carry seven to twenty times the payload. With the short distances between British cities the speed advantage is minimized so long as airports have to be remote from the centres of the urban areas. It is only when the distance becomes great, or awkward because of a short sea link such as the Irish Sea or English Channel, that the railway with its connections finds difficulty in holding traffic. It was estimated by P. G. Masefield in his Presidential Address to the Institute of Transport, 1955, that some 40,000 passengers travel between London and Edinburgh by air, which is about one-third of the number going by public road vehicle and one-tenth of those by rail. This traffic is increasing each year and air is obtaining most of the increase. Air has the advantage of speed

[1] E. A. Pratt, *Scottish Canals and Waterways*. London, 1922 (especially Chapter VI).

and, if road fares be taken as standard, then for each hour saved on journey time the passenger pays 8s. (first-class) by rail and 10s. 6d. by air. If time is money Mr. Masefield's figures give a value to it! If helicopters can be used to link the airports with the city centres then much of the time wasted on an air journey will be saved and the cost per-hour-saved will be reduced assuming the present fares are maintained.

Although railways do not tunnel or bridge the English Channel the nationalized concerns on both sides have a lively interest in the traffic; they own steamers as well as operating the connecting rail services. Comparing the five-year periods 1934–8 and 1948–52 the passengers carried by rail steamers rose from $11\frac{1}{4}$ million to $12\frac{1}{4}$ million whereas by air the passengers increased by 463 per cent from under $\frac{3}{4}$ million for the pre-war five years to over 4 million in the post-war period. Air transport on such a link has many advantages over the existing surface routes—speed, cleanliness, guaranteed seats, frequency and wider choice of departure times. The rail-sea service offers in its favour more spacious facilities, including luggage, and better night accommodation. For the shorter journeys to the continent the rail-sea service can still effectively compete but for the longer, such as that from London to Lisbon, the air journey is little, if at all, dearer and is not so fatiguing.

Counteracting Competition

Railway organizations all over the world are forced to consider the rivalry of other transport agencies and they are remodelling their approach to suit the changed conditions. For freight traffic across the Narrow Seas the railways are tending to concentrate on train ferries and container traffic which reduces the cost and time delays and so does provide some rivalry to the faster, but more expensive, air freight services.

Much time has been wasted in railway services in the past by the need to collect and distribute freight traffic from small stations. In Britain this has tended to perpetuate the small wagon and to lead to shunting delays. The modern technique is to provide railheads from which the goods are dispersed and collected by road. The Great Western Railway before the war had zoned in this way most of its territory and had improved its service in districts such as South Wales. Then again, to tap some of the traffic which goes by road in Britain an express runs from King's Cross to Perth carrying private cars while in the U.S.A. loaded lorries are taken south by rail from Chicago. These services run overnight and the railways in this way reduce the time on the journeys for the road drivers rest on the way.

Other forms of active defence against loss of traffic are by improving the trains, in speed and cleanliness, and by lowering fares. When British Railways introduced diesel-units in West Yorkshire in 1954 the number of passengers at once increased and in the U.S.A. the speed and cleanliness of diesels has been found to have the same effect. Lowering of fares has been attempted to a slight degree in post-war Britain. Some of the cheap fare concessions have been re-introduced and special excursions, for example the *Starlight Special*, placed on the London–Edinburgh run using a route to Marylebone Station which was not already congested with traffic.

A defeatist attitude has been adopted over the closing of branches. While it must be admitted that many of these were producing insufficient revenue, to justify their remaining open with the present system of operating, nevertheless there are a number of points which the users, if not the operators, of the railways feel. First, many of these lines were constructed at relatively low capital expense, they approach "surface" lines in the simplicity of their earthworks, and it was never expected that the income per mile would approach that of a main line. Secondly, with shorter working hours, the number of men is greatly increased to keep the lines open and while the number may be justified with an intensive traffic it becomes an impossible burden on a lightly used branch. Signal sections could be increased in length and other economies made without any serious reduction in the safety factor. The standards of maintenance are high in Britain but the wages for the man-power at stations and along many of the branch lines has proved too great. Closing of the branch lines will lead to a loss of traffic on the main lines because passengers forced off one section will no longer tend to continue by rail for the rest of their journey.

British railways have a high reputation for safety; if an accident occurs with even one life lost it is heralded in the papers as "Railway Disaster", and this is much to the credit of the railway organizations.

In time of war, as in peace, railways have proved the best land agency for the mass movement of goods and people. With changing conditions their virtual monopoly has vanished but there are still advantages which allow the iron road, evolved nearly a century and a half ago in the coalfields of Britain, to play a part in meeting the modern transport needs of mankind.

SELECTED BIBLIOGRAPHY

THE following references are suggested for further reading, in addition to those referred to in the text.

General Works

There are many volumes on railways and among these may be instanced:

A. T. Hadley, *Railroad electrification and traffic problems*, New York, 13th Edition, 1902.

A. M. Wellington, *The economic theory of location of railways*, New York, 6th Edition, 1908.

F. A. Talbot, *The railway conquest of the world*, London, 1911.

E. Protheroe, *The railways of the world*, London, 1911.

B. Reed, *Railway engines of the world*, London, 1934.

P. Burtt, *Railway electrification and traffic problems*, London, 1929.

C. Dollfus and E. de Geoffroy, *Histoire de la locomotion terrestre*, Paris, 1935.

C. J. Allen, *The romantic story of the iron road*, London, 1940.

T. F. Cameron, *Outline of railway traffic operation*, London, 1946.

——, *The world's railways*, London, 1947.

H. Peyret, *Histoire des chemins de fer en France et dans le monde*, Paris, 1949.

Periodical publications which contain much of value are *The Railway Magazine*, *Modern Transport* and *The Railway Gazette*. The weekly issues of *Modern Transport* record not only topical changes but also contain abstracts of papers, referring to transport problems, read to technical and learned societies. The special issues of *The Railway Gazette* provide valuable reviews of various countries. *The Financial Times* carries at frequent intervals material of interest to students of transport problems. The articles by "Mercury" in *The Railway Magazine* give useful surveys of train speeds. The bulletins of the *International Congress of Railway Associations* provide much valuable technical information over a wide field. Handbooks issued at regular intervals which contain transport information are *The Railway Yearbook* and *World Railways* (edited by H. Sampson).

British Railways

Volumes on British railways are becoming legion but the following will provide cover for most of the country.

General

F. S. Williams, *Our iron roads*, London, 2nd edit., 1880.

J. P. Pattinson, *British Railways*, London, 1893.

W. M. Acworth, *Railways of England*, London, 5th edit., 1900.

P. Defrance, *Les chemins de fer de la Grande-Bretagne*, Bruxelles, 1911.

E. Cleveland-Stevens, *English Railways*, London, 1915.

C. E. R. Sherrington, *Economics of rail transport in Great Britain*, London, 2 Vols. 1928 and 1937.

C. F. D. Marshall, *A history of British Railways down to the year 1830*, London, 1938.

K. G. Fenelon, *British railways today*, Edinburgh, 1939.

Lord Monkswell, *The railways of Great Britain*, London, 2nd edit., 1926.

O. S. Nock, *The railways of Britain*, London, 1947-8.

K. H. Johnston, *British railways and economic recovery*, London, 1949.

J. St. John, *The railways of Britain*, London, 1954.

Individual companies

C. F. D. Marshall, *A history of the Southern Railway*, London, 1936.

Sir G. Findlay, *The working and management of an English railway* [L.N.W.R.], London, 5th edit., 1894.

W. L. Steel, *History of the L.N.W.R.*, London, 1914.

F. S. Williams, *The Midland Railway*, London, 3rd edit., 1877.

C. E. Stretton, *History of the Midland Railway*, London, 1901.

F. W. Houghton and W. H. Foster, *Story of the Settle–Carlisle Line*, York, 1948.

W. M. Gradon, *Furness Railway*, Altrincham, 1946.

J. W. Williamson, *A British railway behind the scenes* [L.M.S.R.], London, 1933.

The Times, L.M.S.R. Centenary, London, 1938.

C. H. Grinling, *History of the Great Northern Railway*, London, 1898.

W. W. Tomlinson, *The North Eastern Railway*, Newcastle, 1914.

J. S. MacLean, *Newcastle and Carlisle Railway*, Newcastle, 1948.

L.N.E.R., *Trade and commerce of the North East District*, York, 1921.

G. A. Sekon, *History of the G.W.R.*, London, 1895.

E. T. MacDermot, *History of the G.W.R.*, London, 2 vols., 1927–31.

O. S. Nock, *The Great Western Railway*, Cambridge, 1951.

C. P. Gasquoine, *Story of the Cambrian*, Oswestry, 1922.

Scotland

W. M. Acworth, *Railways of Scotland*, London, 1890.

J. W. F. Gardner, *Railway enterprise . . . in Scotland*, Glasgow, 1934.

A. C. O'Dell. "A geographical examination of the development of Scottish railways," *Scot. Geog. Mag.*, lv, 1939, pp. 129–48.

O. S. Nock, *Scottish Railways*, Edinburgh, 1950.

W. McIlwraith, *The Glasgow and South Western Railway*, Glasgow, 1880.

G. Graham, *The Caledonian Railway*, Glasgow, 1888.

R. A. Vallance, *History of the Highland Railway*, London, 1938.

Sir M. Barclay-Harvey, *History of the Great North of Scotland Railway*, London, 1939.

C. H. Ellis, *The North British Railway*, London, 1955.

Ireland

J. C. Conroy, *History of railways in Ireland*, London, 1928.

H. Fayle, *Narrow gauge railways in Ireland*, London, 1946.

European Railways

A. Picard, *Les chemins de fer français*, Paris, 6 vols., 1884–5.

C. J. Allen, *Switzerland's amazing railways*, Edinburgh, 1953.

E. Gut [Edit.], *Les mystères des chemins de fer*, Lausanne, 1946.

——, *100 Jahre Schweitzer Eisenbahn*, Zürich, 1947.

——, *Hundert Jahre Deutsche Eisenbahnen*, Berlin, 1935.

——, *Statens Järnvägar* 1906–31 [Sweden], Stockholm, 2 vols., 1931.

J. Broch, *Av Norges Statsbanens Historie*, Oslo, 3 parts, 1935–7.

J. Broch, *Av Bergensbanens Historie*, Oslo, 3 parts, 1932–4.

——, *Stambanen gjennom Nord-Norge*, Bodø, 1949.

N. Buxton, "Balkan geography and Balkan railways", *Geog. Journ.*, xxxii, 1908, pp. 217–39.

S. H. Beaver, "Railways in the Balkan peninsula", *Geog, Journ.*, xcvii, pp. 273–94.

F. Wais, *Origen de los ferrocarriles españoles*, Madrid, 1949.

——, *Les chemins de fer en U.R.S.S.* [Inst. Nat. de la Statistique et des Études Économiques], Paris, 1946.

North American Railways

——, *Railways of America*, London, 1890.

S. Dunbar, *History of travel in America*, New York, 1937.

E. A. Pratt, *American railways*, London, 1903.

F. H. Spearman, *Strategy of great railroads*, London, 1905.

——, *Study of domestic land and water transportation* : *Hearings before Sub-Committee*, Washington, 2 vols., 1950.

E. Hungerford, *Story of the Baltimore and Ohio Railroad*, New York, 2 vols., 1928.

R. C. Overton, *Burlington West*, Cambridge (Mass.), 1941.

S. G. Reed, *History of the Texas Railroads*, Houston, 1941.

J. M. Gibbon, *Steel of Empire* [C.P.R.], London, 1935.

Geol. Surv., *Transcontinental Excursion via C.P.R. and C.N.R.*, Ottawa, 1913.

W. F. A. Turgeon, *Report of the Royal Commission on* [*Canadian*] *Transportation*, Ottawa, 1911.

Bulletins of the Railway and Locomotive Historical Society, Boston (Mass.)

Publications of the Association of American Railroads.

African Railways

J. van der Poel, *Railway and Customs policies in South Africa, 1885–1910*, London, 1933.

M. F. Hill, *Permanent Way, story of the Kenya and Uganda Railway*, Nairobi, 1949.

Much material exists for the railways of Asia, South America and Australasia in the books listed under *General* above.

E—English usage.
A—American usage.

Angle-iron (A):	Equivalent to fishplate (E).
Ballast (E and A):	Material to spread load and improve drainage.
Baseplate (E):	To spread weight of load and to prevent cutting into sleepers.
Caboose (A):	Van for conductor (A), guard (E).
Car (A):	Equivalent to passenger coach (E), and to covered wagon (E).
Cross-tie (A):	Equivalent to sleeper (E).
Fishplate (E):	To hold rail ends together.
Railroad (A):	Synonymous with railway. Of 134 Class I companies in the U.S.A., 63 are railway and 66 are railroad in their title; 5 use neither.
Sleeper (E):	Timber to carry rails and hold at correct gauge.
Tie-plates (A):	Equivalent to Baseplate (E).

ABBREVIATIONS

B.R.	British Railways.
C.N.R.	Canadian National Railway.
C.P.R.	Canadian Pacific Railway.
G.C.R.	Great Central Railway.
G.E.R.	Great Eastern Railway.
G.N.R.	Great Northern Railway.
G.W.R.	Great Western Railway.
L.M.S.R.	London, Midland & Scottish Railway.
L.N.W.R.	London and North Western Railway.
L. & Y.R.	Lancashire and Yorkshire Railway.
M.R.	Midland Railway.
Monon	Chicago, Indianapolis & Louisville Railway.
N.B.R.	North British Railway.
N.E.R.	North Eastern Railway.
N.Y.	New York.
Rly.	Railway.
R.R.	Railroad.
S.E.R.	South Eastern Railway.
S.R.	Southern Railway.

199

*MODERN COLONIZATION
R. J. Harrison Church
Lecturer in Geography at the London School of Economics and Political Science

THE BRITISH BANKING MECHANISM
W. Manning Dacey
Economic Adviser, Lloyds Bank

NATIONAL INCOME AND SOCIAL ACCOUNTING
H. C. Edey
Lecturer in Accounting and Business Finance, University of London

and

Alan T. Peacock
Reader in Public Finance, University of London

INTERNATIONAL MONETARY CO-OPERATION 1945–56
Brian Tew
Professor of Economics, University of Nottingham

IN PREPARATION—FOR PUBLICATION IN 1957–58

THE GEOGRAPHY OF AIR TRANSPORT
K. R. Sealy
Lecturer in Geography at the London School of Economics and Political Science

THE GEOGRAPHY OF THE PORT OF LONDON
James Bird
Assistant Lecturer in Geography, King's College, University of London

THE GEOGRAPHY OF POPULATION
H. C. Brookfield
Lecturer in Geography, University of New England, Armidale, New South Wales

These volumes will be published at 10s. 6d. net each